Charles F. Kettering

A Biography

Charles F. Kettering

A Biography

by THOMAS ALVIN BOYD

with a forward by
ALFRED P. SLOAN, JR.

BeardBooks
Washington, D.C.

To

My Wife
Grace Bethel Boyd

The original title of this work was:

Professional Amateur:
The Biography of
Charles Franklin Kettering

The title has been changed to facilitate electronic retrieval and/or to reflect current conditions in the subject area.

Cover photo image furnished by
Scarchburg Archives, Kettering University

FOREWORD

It has been said that the only purpose of a preface or introduction to a book is to save the reviewer the mental effort of reading the book as a whole. I do not know how true that may be, but I do know that any preface or introduction that anyone, let alone myself, could write to this remarkable story would be overshadowed by the substance of the narrative itself. Its significance, to my mind, is twofold: first, the lesson to be learned; second, the story itself.

Progress has come about only when here and there an unusual man broke loose and independently, on his own, started something different. The usual man seldom makes the inventions, or strikes out in new directions or blazes new trails, or advances our frontiers of knowledge and understanding. Such things are done by unusual men who have particular talent, broader vision, more imagination, more ambition, willingness to work, courage to act independently and according to the force of their own convictions, especially in the face of the ever present antagonism to change. The significant thing is that while the unusual man may profit by his unusual efforts and sacrifice, in an infinitely greater measure does he contribute to the advancement of the whole. Indeed, that is the only way the whole can ever advance.

Perhaps the reader may well say, this has nothing to do with the story. But, on the other hand, the story is the biography of a most unusual individual. It is hard to visualize, let alone appraise in definite terms, the contribution to our progress that Charles F. Kettering has made, not only in a material sense but in a philosophical sense as well. Everyone, especially those having responsibility in the higher level of affairs will, I am sure, pay tribute to his outstanding contribution to the advancement of American society.

Charles F. Kettering was born in the hills of northern Ohio. His parents were farmers. As a young man he taught school to finance himself educationally. He ultimately entered The Ohio State University where he graduated at the age of twenty-eight. He was very definitely handicapped by poor eyesight, which forced him to withdraw from the University in his sophomore year. This made it difficult for him to read and study, in the normal sense. In the meantime he entered employment with a local telephone company—not in the office, but in the field. His duty was to "fix" things. And ironically speaking, he has been "fixing" things ever since. That was really the beginning of his productive career as an experimenter and trail blazer.

It has been my privilege to be associated with "Ket"—as we call him—for over forty years. He has been a great inspiration to me throughout these forty years. And even now, when we are both retired from active service, we are still associated together in medical research.

To outline in detail his accomplishments—diversified and extraordinary as they really are—is not the purpose of this introduction. That belongs to the narrative itself. Therefore, with these few words of admiration and gratitude, I present to you, the reader—Charles F. Kettering, farmer, schoolteacher, mechanic, inventor, engineer, scientist, social philosopher and, superimposed upon all—master salesman.

ALFRED P. SLOAN, JR.

TABLE OF CONTENTS

ILLUSTRATIONS

xi

IL_USTRATIONS

PROFESSIONAL AMATEUR

INTRODUCTION

MORE THAN SIXTY YEARS AGO, on a wooden wall in the basement of the Loudonville, Ohio, High School, two classmates carved their names, one above the other:

GAILLARD FULLER
CHARLIE KETTERING

After the first name was cut a skull and crossbones, signifying that Gaillard meant to be a doctor, which he became. After the second name was carved a question mark. By turning out to be a twentieth-century Benjamin Franklin, Charlie Kettering has since brilliantly answered that question.

*Farm boy and later country schoolteacher, Kettering became an eminent engineer, industrial pioneer, and apostle of progress. "I am not pleading with you to make changes," he early began telling men in industry. "I am telling you you have got to make them—not because I say so, but because old Father Time will take care of you if you don't change. . . . Consequently you need a procurement department for new ideas."

As for himself, he has always operated a department of that kind. Working first at the National Cash Register Company, then as an independent inventor, and afterward for twenty-seven years as vice-president and head of research for

General Motors, he has done much creative work. Boss Ket, as he is affectionately called by those associated with him, electrified the cash register, developed a new multiple-counter bank machine and the first successful electric self-starter for automobiles, as well as the system of battery ignition used today.

He guided the development of "Ethyl" gasoline; of the high-compression automobile engine; of the nontoxic and noninflammable refrigerant, "Freon"; of better and longer lasting finishes for automobiles; and of many other products, including the improved diesel engine which, in one of its applications, has revolutionized the powering of railroads. With the resources that came to him from many creative endeavors, he also organized the Charles F. Kettering Foundation through which he and his associates are searching out new knowledge for the benefit of mankind.

In making such searches, he has said, "We are simply professional amateurs. We are amateurs because we are doing things for the first time. We are professional because we know we are going to have a lot of trouble. . . . The price of progress is trouble. And I don't think the price is too high."

Besides his manifold activities in science and engineering, Kettering is businessman, banker, educator, philosopher, and public speaker. Concerning business, he has said, "I am for the double-profit system, a reasonable profit for the manufacturer and a much greater profit for the customer." Education is one of his principal interests and concerns, and he aids it and guides it in every way he can. "My definition of an educated man," he says, "is the fellow who knows the right thing to do at the time it has to be done. . . . You can be sincere and still be stupid."

As speaker, much of what Kettering has to say relates to the future. "I object to people running down the future," he has said. "I am going to live all the rest of my life there,

4

and I would like it to be a nice place, polished, bright, glistening, and glorious."

Kettering particularly likes to speak to audiences of young people. To one such group he expressed his optimistic and forward-looking thinking in these words:

What I believe is that, by proper effort, we can make the future almost anything we want to make it.

In reality, we have only begun to knock a few chips from the great quarry of knowledge that has been given us to dig out and use. We are like the two fellows who started to walk from New York to San Francisco. When they got over into New Jersey, one said: "We must be pretty nearly there. We have been walking a long, long time."

That is just how we are in what we know technically. We have just barely begun.

I wish I could say, in language so dramatic that it would impress you deeply, what I think our opportunities are. The best words I can find for doing so are these: *This is the golden age of opportunity, the age of opportunity unlimited!*

Nothing can better show the truth of this statement than the life of the uncommon man whose story is told in the following pages.

T. A. Boyd

PART I

Early Years

1876–1904

I

CHARLES FRANKLIN KETTERING was born in a farmhouse among the hills of northern Ohio on August 29, 1876. Franklin was chosen as his middle name after an uncle of his. But, if it had stood instead for Benjamin Franklin, it would have been prophetic of what he was to become.

Charlie Kettering's birth came during a period of transition in the development of the nation. That summer, one hundred years after the signing of the Declaration of Independence, the papers were filled with accounts of the great Centennial Exhibition at Philadelphia. Mark Twain's *Tom Sawyer* was published, and so was the song, *I'll Take You Home Again, Kathleen*. That year the telephone was invented by Alexander Graham Bell; and the four-stroke cycle gas engine, later to be used universally in automobiles and elsewhere, was brought into being by Nikolaus Otto in Germany. The country stood then on the threshold of vast industrial expansion and revolutionary technological advances. Although young Charlie Kettering was destined to play an important part in bringing about these events, this fact made little difference then in the quiet routine of the Kettering family.

On the side of his father, Jacob, Charlie Kettering's grandparents had come to America about 1835. They were Alsatians, part French and part German. Some of the same family settled in England, and the town of Kettering in Northampton is named for them. His mother, Martha Hunter Kettering, was of Scotch-Irish descent. But, as he remarked in later life, "All we knew about the Ketterings and the

I don't think so !

9

Hunters was that they all had to work hard for a living."

Jacob Kettering was a capable farmer. He was a carpenter, too—one of those carpenters with the old-time skill of laying out the framework of large timbers used then in building houses and barns. With nothing but a steel square and a piece of blue chalk—no drawings at all, only a picture in his mind—he could mark off each of the many pieces of the framework to show how it was to be formed. When cut to size and mortised and tenoned in accordance with those blue-line markings, the parts would fit together precisely like the pieces of a jigsaw puzzle. With a wooden peg through each joint they made a solid skeleton for a building. Farmer and carpenter, Jacob Kettering was also prominent and active enough in community affairs to have once been elected a commissioner of Ashland County, Ohio.

Martha Hunter Kettering was a quiet person with the all-round capabilities of an intelligent country woman in her time. Something of her temperament is suggested by a conversation she had in later years with her son Charlie's associate, Dr. F. O. Clements, who had accompanied him on a visit to her farm home. By then Charlie Kettering, as one of the early leaders of aviation, was doing so much flying that his mother was greatly concerned about his safety. She pleaded with Dr. Clements to use his influence to get Charlie to stop flying. He told her that he could not very well do that because Kettering's work at that time was largely with airplanes, and he needed to have personal experience with them. Hearing this, Mrs. Kettering was quiet for a moment. Then, with a smile, she said: "Do you suppose Charlie would take me up in his airplane?"

The white Kettering farmhouse, partly covered with ivy and shaded by pine trees, with its small yard and surrounding fields and woods, was a typical setting for a rural American boyhood in that time. It was situated three miles from the village of Loudonville. A part of the Kettering farm has been in continuous possession of the family connection ever since it had belonged to the Indians. The original deed, or patent record, was signed by President James Madison in 1816. In later years that farm came into the possession of Charlie Kettering himself, and he owns it still. Although situated in a hilly part of the state, a considerable portion of it is excellent farm land, well lying and fertile.

The life of young Kettering was not different from that of other country boys of that time and place, except as his turn of mind made it different. He had two brothers, Adam and David, and two sisters, Emma and Daisy. All had to begin early to help with the chores. Among the several duties which fell to the lot of Charlie were keeping the woodbox full and feeding the sheep. Everyone took part, too, in the major work of the farm and the household—raising corn, wheat, and potatoes, harvesting hay, milking the cows, churning the butter, and doing the many other things that filled so full the days of farm people.

Kettering remembers that he liked particularly the work connected with growing corn. "I liked everything about raising corn," he said once, "planting it, plowing it, cutting it, and everything else. I liked to go barefoot when plowing corn. The ground felt so good, even though once in a while a fellow did hit a stone." To some of those who gathered at the Kettering farm for the celebration of his seventieth birthday, he boasted that he had been "the best darn corncutter in Ohio." This was of course well before the time when modern machinery came to the farm.

A rarely told story of Kettering's corn-growing days goes as follows:

"My father and I were plowing corn one day alongside the road when a neighbor came by in his wagon and stopped to chat a while, as farmers do. To my father he said, 'Jake, I sold my hogs today.'

" 'Did you?' said my father. 'How did they weigh?'

" 'Well, they didn't weigh as much as I thought they would —and I didn't have any idea they would either.' "

Unlike most boys, Charlie interested himself in tasks his mother performed. He took care of her sewing machine, oiling it—and also taking it apart to see how it was made. He operated it, too, by winding bobbins for his mother and by doing plain sewing for her as well. Once he even cut out a dress from a pattern and sewed it up on the machine. In the catalogue from which his mother bought that sewing machine when he was a small boy he read the story of Elias Howe and his invention of the sewing machine; and all his life he remembered that story.

He learned how to knit also, and he recalled that he used to cast on knitting for his mother. In later life he once astonished his sister-in-law, Mrs. Ralph D. Williams, who was knitting some article and remarked that she did not know quite how to cast off or form the finished edge. "I'll show you how to do it," Kettering said. And he did.

Among the animals on the farm, Charlie had a special liking for cats that has remained with him all his life. He thinks cats are more intelligent than dogs. On the farm he had some two dozen cats at one time. Going off to school in the morning, he would admonish his mother to be sure to feed Tommy and Trixie and his other cats. He took excellent care of them, even to treating their sore eyes using an eye dropper. And, when one of the cats died, he and his sister Daisy would put it in a box for a coffin, bury it with proper ceremony, and put flowers on its grave.

As he grew up on the farm, living close to wild and growing things as country boys do, and spending much of his time out of doors, Charlie Kettering watched, observed, and noticed many things that made him wonder. The mystery of the growth of plants challenged him and has fascinated him ever since. There was a keener, more insistent curiosity in him than in most boys. One summer, when he had earned a fair amount of money helping a neighbor cut wheat, he bought a microscope, and with it spent much time examining and identifying the weeds and plants that grew on the farm. He found that there were different kinds of goldenrod. There was even a difference, he noticed, between the goldenrod that grew on the east side of certain fences and that growing on the west side. His strong interest in plants and how they grow led on to the extensive studies he has made or sponsored in later life on the problem of photosynthesis—or, as he has expressed it, "Why is the grass green?"

Looking out from his mother's kitchen window, he wondered why it was that he could see through glass. That is a mystery which has puzzled him all of his life and about which he has spoken many times. "If you look in the dictionary," he would say, "you will see that it is because glass is transparent. But if you look up the word 'transparent,' you will learn that the meaning of it is something you can see through."

Helping one summer to put up the hay, Charlie made a misstep which caused him to tumble out of the haymow, breaking his right arm. In the weeks following, as he went around the farm with his broken arm in a sling, he became skillful in using his left hand. This led him to develop what later became astonishing versatility. Not only can he write with either hand but he can also write one thing with his right hand while simultaneously writing something else with his left. He can write upside down or in mirror image, and in general make each of his hands do independently just what his brain directs. He does it, he says, by thinking quickly back and forth from one hand to the other.

The life of the Ketterings on that quiet farm three miles from town and off the main roads was simple indeed by the standards of today. As in most farm families of five children in the late 1800's, money was not plentiful; but still the family was not in want of anything necessary. Like his brothers and other country boys of the time, Charlie went barefoot in summer. In wintertime, at home on the farm and walking to school and back, he wore leather boots—boots the toes of which were tipped with metal to keep them from being kicked out too fast.

It was around the boots he wore as a boy that in later years he reconstructed, in the following words, one of the most revealing recollections of his boyhood:

I am enthusiastic about being an American because I came from the hills in Ohio. I was a hillbilly. We each had one pair of boots a year; and we didn't put them on too soon in the fall because we had to decide which we would sooner do, run around in the frosty grass a little more in the fall or in the wet snow in the spring.

Now, I didn't know at that time that I was an underprivileged person because I had to drive the cows through the frosty grass and stand in a nice warm spot where a cow had lain to warm my feet. I thought that was wonderful. I walked three miles to the high school in a little village and I thought that was wonderful, too. I thought of all that as opportunity, and I thought the only thing involved in opportunity was whether I knew how to think with my head and how to do with my hands. I thought that was what opportunity consisted of. I didn't know you had to have money. I didn't know you had to have all these luxuries that we want everybody to have today.

At the early time of which Kettering here spoke he naturally had no notion of the big opportunities that later were to come to him or of the notable use he was to make of them.

II

FROM THE TIME Charlie Kettering was six until he was nearly fifteen, he attended the country school in his district. Before long, though, great changes were to come in country schools, as in other aspects of rural life. Charlie and his brothers and sisters were members of the last generation of farm children —or perhaps the next to the last—which got its education in the one-room country school, as it had existed in the United States for so many, many years. Not long after the Kettering children attended it, the old-time country school was largely supplanted by the consolidated school.

That change was brought about in large part by the coming of the automobile and the motorbus, to which Kettering himself later made important contributions. But the abandonment of the country schoolhouse brought to an end one of the most memorable and influential institutions of country life in the early years of the nation.

The building in which the Kettering children attended school was typical of those in the country at the time. Called Big Run and situated over the hill about a mile from the Kettering home, it was a one-room wooden building with a door at the end nearer the road and three windows on each side. On top of the schoolhouse sat a belfry with a bell which rang for school to "take up" and to "let out," and which at the end of the "noon" and "recess" periods of play called the "scholars" reluctantly back to their books.

The schoolroom was heated by a potbellied cast-iron coal stove sitting in the middle of the room. On cold winter days that stove sometimes was fired so vigorously that it, and even the lower section of the smoke pipe above it, would get red hot. Four rows of double desks faced the front. As there was a jackknife in the pocket of almost every schoolboy, the wooden tops and sides of the desks were marred by carved initials and other designs.

All the school-age youth of the district went to school in that same room, children from six years old to young men and women up to eighteen, or even older. The desks were accordingly graduated in height from the back of the room to the front. On the seats toward the front there was often much swinging of restless young feet; for, with only one teacher for all the pupils, the younger children had little to do between recitations.

On the wall across the front of the schoolroom was a blackboard consisting of a wide strip of smooth plaster painted black. On that blackboard Charlie used to work out problems in arithmetic and diagram sentences in grammar. In an address at Loudonville in 1940, Kettering recalled that he could "remember just as well as if it were today some of the mottoes we used to write on the old blackboard."

Charlie was studious, but he had the handicap of being nearsighted and not yet having glasses to correct it. So he had to hold the book he was studying quite close to his eyes. Still, he learned some things merely by hearing the other children recite. The multiplication table was one. He learned it mostly by listening to the other children repeating it over and over so many times—children not quite so quick in mind as he.

McGuffey's readers were the standard texts in Charlie's school, as in so many others at that time. He thus learned to read by studying such time-honored classics of poetry and prose as "Meddlesome Mattie," "The Old Oaken Bucket," "Hugh Idle and Mister Toil," and "The Blind Men and the Elephant." In the *Sixth Reader* poem, "The Barefoot Boy"

16

by Whittier, Charlie read a description of himself as a farm
boy in the summertime:

> Blessings on thee, little man,
> Barefoot boy, with cheeks of tan!
> With thy turned-up pantaloons,
> And thy merry whistled tunes;
> With thy red lip, redder still
> Kissed by strawberries on the hill;
> With the sunshine on thy face,
> Through thy torn brim's jaunty grace . . .

The stories in McGuffey's readers often had morals—morals
which were likely to be stated as such. As a boy in Big Run
School, Charlie was thus told that Mister Toil, as the per-
sonification of work, is everywhere, even in the most splendid
mansions and in places of entertainment and gaiety; that he
cannot be avoided; but that, when one comes to know him
aright, he is a good fellow after all. In the lesson entitled
"Poverty and Riches" he read that even the poorest boy is
rich in the things that really count: his sight, his hearing,
his good health, and many other priceless possessions. Charlie
was taught, too, that "Where There Is a Will There Is a
Way." And, after a lifetime of experience of his own, it is
Kettering's philosophy that "we can overcome the difficulties
if we want to."

Among Charlie Kettering's teachers at Big Run School
were two of the three men who in his estimation had the
greatest influence on his early education. The first of these
two gifted teachers was John Rowe. When in arithmetic the
class came to square root, "Professor" Rowe did not teach
the square root formula as a mere abstract rule. Instead, he
brought to school a piece of cherry board and had the class
saw it into blocks which proved to eyes as well as minds
what the taking of square root really means. That lesson laid

17

the foundation of a simple rule Kettering has followed all his life and which he once expressed in these words: "I think we must have facts and understanding before a 'formula' education means anything at all." He has never been one to say he understands anything unless or until he has found the *why* of it.

The second teacher at Big Run School who had a major influence upon Charlie was Neil McLaughlin, a man who later was to recommend him as a schoolteacher. When the class in history was studying about Christopher Columbus, for instance, McLaughlin did not teach merely that Columbus discovered America in 1492. He encouraged the pupils to find out why Columbus sailed, what obstacles he had to overcome, how he got backing for the enterprise, how many and what kind of vessels he had, where he landed, and what the land there was like when Columbus and his men stepped ashore.

Neil McLaughlin taught his pupils "to think in and around and through," Kettering recalled. "Youngsters naturally have exploring minds," he has also said, expressing his philosophy of education. "They should be encouraged to quest and question. The trouble is we don't get interested in the commonplace things, and it is the commonplace things that go to make up the universe."

About a stone's throw from Big Run schoolhouse stood Wolf's Mill. That old gristmill, driven by a huge water wheel with the rhythmic splashing of water at the bottom of it, interested Charlie, and he spent much time there. Besides learning about water power and flour mills, he got from the wise old miller some bits of philosophy which he stored in his young mind. "A lot of people are bound to worry," the miller once told him. "If you can do something about it, you ought to worry. I would think there was something wrong with you if you didn't. But if you can't do anything, then

The farm home in which Charles F. Kettering was born and lived as a boy.

Kettering homestead, as he rebuilt it on the site of his boyhood home.

Charlie Kettering when he graduated from high school in the summer of 1895.

Edward A. Deeds when, in 1904, as an executive of the National Cash Register Company, he sought out Kettering and hired him.

worrying is just like running this mill when there is no grist to grind. All that does is to wear out the mill."

In 1891, when Charlie Kettering was fifteen, he entered the high school in Loudonville. A tall gangling boy, his near-sightedness gave him a somewhat stumbling gait, and at first the boys and girls from town were inclined to laugh at him. Each day he walked the three miles from the farm into Loudonville and back, through sun and rain and snow. The bottoms of his pants legs were sometimes painted with the mud through which he had come. But young Kettering's brilliance and friendliness soon won a place for him among his fellow students. "We had fun and he had fun with us," recalled his classmate Gaillard Fuller, who became the seventh Fuller to serve the people of Loudonville as a physician.

In those daily walks back and forth between the farm and the high school, Charlie often stopped at the big flour mill in the town which was powered not by a water wheel but by a Corliss steam engine. He made friends with the men who tended the engine and ran the mill, and they taught him many practical things.

In his studies at the high school, Charlie was especially good in mathematics and physics. Dr. Fuller remembers the sureness with which Charlie used to demonstrate propositions in geometry and the clarity with which he gave his proofs of the correctness of the demonstrations. He did not care so much what the answer to a problem was, but he wanted to be sure that he knew the reason for it and how it was arrived at.

He kept working at things until he got them. In an early and unexpected test in Latin, he and every other member of his class flunked. Afterwards, while plowing at home on the farm when school was not in session, Charlie fastened his Latin grammar to the handles of the plow and tied the book open with a piece of binder twine. As he went round and round the field that day, turning over the pleasant-smelling earth, he learned that part of Latin grammar so thoroughly that he did not fail in any later examination.

Charlie was sociable and always willing to help other members of his class. If a little group was seen around him in the hallway, it was as likely as not that he was reading for them the Latin assignment for that day. No one else in his class cared much for physics. And when, for some reason, the members of the physics class were more than usually ill-prepared, Charlie would ask questions of the teacher, C. E. Budd, who was also principal of the high school and who became a lifelong friend of Charlie's. He would try in that way to get discussion started to fill up the period, thereby saving his fellow students from having to recite.

On Friday afternoons the school held literary programs in which the students gave recitations, read essays they had written, or took part in debates. Charlie's classmates remembered that he was a good debater and able to hold his own in any argument. Sometimes, when not debating himself, he would aid a member of his class by preparing an outline to help him in upholding his side of the debate.

One winter Charlie was chosen to represent the Loudonville High School in an oratorical contest at the nearby college town of Wooster. "Every person . . . has an ideal," he said in part on that occasion. "A large number of persons see their ideal in fashion. . . . The sum of their thoughts is: Bang and dress and friz, and friz and dress and bang. . . . And what becomes of such people? Did you ever hear of any of them rising to eminence? It would not be so hard for them to die if they could only arrange their funeral dress."

Commencement came in 1895 for Charlie Kettering and his classmates at the Loudonville High School. For that big event all the boys in the class ordered suits just alike from the tailor shop in the town, the first tailor-made suits any of them had ever had, with long cutaway coats, bound with braid, and with tails coming down to the level of the knees or below.

At the graduation exercises each member of the class gave a ten-minute oration, with the result that the program was extremely long. It extended from 7:30 in the evening until after midnight. Charlie's oration had for its title the class motto, "Yet Gleaners." Even though his classmates and he had now finished high school, he said, they should continue to gather knowledge, an admonition which he was himself to follow avidly in the years ahead.

But the learning Kettering acquired during his high school years was not limited to that obtained in the old brick school building. Speaking in 1946 to the large gathering assembled at Loudonville as a community celebration of his seventieth birthday, he said: "I had the privilege—not the task—of going to the Loudonville High School. I had the privilege of going past the Loudonville mill, too, and there I learned about Corliss engines. There is a great difference between knowing a thing and understanding it. You can know a lot and not really understand anything. But from those practical men there in that mill and elsewhere I learned how to understand things."

III

In the fall after Kettering had graduated from the Loudonville High School he became teacher of a country school. He was then nineteen years old. The school, called Bunker Hill, was situated over the hills five miles from the Kettering home. It was a typical one-room country school like Big Run which he had attended just a few years earlier.

There were then about thirty pupils in Bunker Hill School. They ranged from beginners to young men and women eighteen or nineteen years old. Thus the teacher was scarcely older than some of his pupils. As was the custom in country schools, he had to teach everything from the ABC's through reading, spelling, geography, history, and grammar to advanced arithmetic.

Because some of the older boys at Bunker Hill had made trouble for teachers in the past, the school had the reputation of being tough and hard to control. For that reason the new teacher began sternly by putting a big switch in a conspicuous place at the front of the schoolroom and laying down some rules. He would thrash the first pupil who broke one of those rules, he threatened.

But that was mere bluff, as he afterwards confessed to Andy Easly, one of his pupils. In reality, he could not thrash anyone, he said. And, as it turned out, he did not have to, for soon he was admired by everyone. Always out with pupils at playtime, he liked particularly to play ball and to skate.

Kettering did not follow slavishly the teaching practices of the time. Instead of teaching spelling, for instance, solely by having the class memorize the spellings of a group of

22

words in the spelling book, he would sometimes vary the assignment by having his pupils read something in the *Saturday Evening Post* and tell them that they would be expected to know how to spell the words contained in it. He wanted their study of spelling to be not detached and abstract but tied in with something concrete, something of interest to them.

In afteryears he told of having once been in a village store looking over some books he found there. When he asked to buy two of them, the keeper of the store remarked: "Mister, them ain't readin' books, them's schoolbooks." But even as a young teacher in Bunker Hill School, Kettering thought that, in so far as possible, schoolbooks ought to be "readin' " books too.

So it was his habit to comment on the lesson as a means of adding to the interest and the understanding of the class. When the class in McGuffey's *Fifth Reader* came to that poem, "Forty Years Ago," he made a suggestion which had an interesting aftermath. The first stanza of that poem is this:

> I've wandered to the village, Tom,
>   I've sat beneath the tree,
> Upon the schoolhouse playground,
>   That sheltered you and me;
> But none was left to greet me, Tom,
>   And few were left to know,
> Who played with me upon the green,
>   Just forty years ago.

After the class had read that stanza, the teacher suggested that each of them make a mental note of the fifteen members of the class and the date; and that, forty years afterward, they find out how many of their number were still living. One member of that class, Emma Coble (later Mrs. J. B. Smith) found forty years afterward that thirteen of the fifteen, as well as the teacher, were still alive and well.

Even there in that country school some of Kettering's instruction went beyond the schoolbooks. "I can remember just as well as yesterday," he said once, "the first time we tried to teach little things relative to agriculture. . . . We had the kids try whether it made any difference as to what phase of the moon they planted corn. . . . We had them try if it made any difference whether the grain of corn was planted up or down, north, east, south, or west. Nobody knew whether it made any difference; that was the reason we tried it."

Soon he was waited on by some of the parents, who said, "We want you to understand that we know all about corn planting. We want you to teach our boys and girls the stuff that is in the books, not this stuff we know all about."

To avoid criticism and yet teach some other subjects in which he and the pupils were interested, the young teacher began to conduct class at night. Once in a while the boys and girls who wanted to do so met with him in the schoolhouse in the evening, and he told them about such subjects as electricity, gravity, sound, and heat. He explained the differential gear, the eccentric, and other things mechanical He also demonstrated by simple experiments some of the facts he was telling the young people.

That year there came to Loudonville a California land promotion car, "Santa Clara County on Wheels," exhibiting the fruits and vegetables of California. As an attraction to get people to view the exhibit, the car carried an X-ray machine, X rays having been discovered by the German, Wilhelm Roentgen, only a few months before that time. So one Friday afternoon the teacher dismissed school at recess time and with the older boys and girls walked the five miles to Loudonville to visit the California car on the railroad siding there.

They went to see not the products of California but the

24

X-ray machine. It thrilled each of them to see the bones in a person's hand through the flesh. It was a wrench for the inquisitive young teacher to leave without a chance to make a closer examination of that fascinating device.

But the minister of a church in the Bunker Hill School community objected to what the teacher had done. "If the Lord had intended people to see through their bodies," said the minister, "he would have given them that kind of eyes. That infernal machine is nothing but the work of the devil, and the young man who took the pupils out of school to see it is not the person to be teaching our young ones."

That charge caused a furor in the community. But the young teacher went serenely on his way, and before long the storm blew over. By the time the school year came to an end, he had proved himself to be one of the best and most loved teachers Bunker Hill School had ever had. Everyone hoped that he would return the next year. But, as things turned out, he did not.

Kettering went off to attend summer school at the College of Wooster, in Wooster, Ohio. There he took just one subject, Greek. His parents wanted him to be a minister; and he went to Wooster to begin preparation.

In that summer term he took a whole year of work in Greek. He did his studying with a fellow student, Lyman C. Knight, who later became a professor at Wooster College, where he spent most of his life. It was at Kettering's suggestion that the two young men studied their Greek assignments together. And Knight was glad for the suggestion because, as he expressed it, he had fallen in love with Charlie Kettering at first sight, having sized him up as a fellow who would be sure to get along. Kettering was all for business, said Knight, and always impatient to get at the study of

Greek. And, as he said too, they really did study Greek that summer, in most intensive fashion.

During that summer at Wooster, Kettering happened to see an Ohio State University catalogue. From it he learned that in the courses in engineering at the university blacksmithing and shop practice were taught, among other subjects. He really had very little understanding then of what engineering was, but if the engineering course had blacksmithing in it he could understand that, for many times he had taken the farm horses to the blacksmith shop to be shod. There he watched the blacksmith heat a horseshoe or some other iron part to a cherry red in his glowing forge and then hammer it into shape with ringing blows on his anvil. Since Kettering preferred blacksmithing to preaching, that catalogue filled him with ambition to attend Ohio State.

But by the time the end of that summer term was near he had a flare-up of serious trouble with his eyes. His brother Adam went to Wooster to bring him home. And, although Adam found his brother half blind and with a splitting headache, he had difficulty getting Charlie to consent to leave the college.

At home his mother and his sisters Emma and Daisy kept cold packs on his eyes and treated him as best they could. Soon Emma took him to the neighboring city of Mansfield to see a physician. The doctor gave him some drops for his eyes and cautioned him to be very careful, to stay in a dark room for some time, and not to read at all. There was fear that he might lose his eyesight altogether. Nevertheless, his brother Adam remembers that when the family was out of the room Charlie got hold of a botany book and tried to read anyway. He wanted to see whether what he had surmised about the cheeseweed's being a cousin of the hollyhock was correct.

Although his eyes had always been weak, this was the first

really serious siege of trouble he had had. It was serious trouble indeed, and unfortunately it was not by any means the last.

Through the late summer and early fall Kettering's eyes improved slowly. But the consequence of the summer's experience was that he did not return to Bunker Hill School. However, about the middle of the school year, 1896–97, he felt able to take a place as teacher of the upper room in the two-room village school at Mifflin, Ohio. Mifflin was a town of about 200 persons situated ten miles from the Kettering home.

He was invited to go there on the recommendation of Neil McLaughlin—the same man who had been one of his best teachers in the country school, Big Run. It was, in fact, McLaughlin's place at Mifflin which Kettering took, for McLaughlin had resigned at the middle of the school year to change from schoolteaching to banking in Loudonville.

That upper room in the two-room Mifflin school was dignified by the name "high school," but in actuality it consisted of the upper grades of the elementary school. However, Kettering was thus in a way the principal of the school. On this account his age was a handicap to him at first—he was only twenty, and he had taken the place of a much older man.

Here he continued to teach as he had in the country school. He told stories to supplement what was in the schoolbooks. Even then he had the gift of illuminating almost any subject with interesting and vivid comments.

Earlis Snyder, who attended school in Mifflin at the time, remembers that a mannerism of Kettering's in the schoolroom was to stand with a thumb in his left pants pocket and a short pointer in his right hand which he used to emphasize what he was saying. He was strict but full of fun. There were big boys in the town school, too, some of them as big as the teacher. But there he put up no switch in the school-room. He was able to keep order merely by the force of his personality and his popularity with pupils.

He taught at Mifflin longer than that half year, returning in the fall for a full year. That second year his sister Emma came to Mifflin with him and taught the lower room of the school.

In the months at Mifflin, it was Kettering's activities outside the schoolroom, however, which most rapidly advanced his own education. One of those influences was the hours he spent at Robinson's drugstore conducting experiments in elementary chemistry and electricity. Taking part in those experiments with him were the experimental-minded druggist, John Robinson, and another young schoolteacher, George G. Gruenwald.

Their experiments with electricity were simple ones made, as Kettering expressed it, "with a couple of dry cells, a doorbell, and a few things like that." But he did learn something about electricity. He experimented with an electric current flowing through a few turns of wire around an iron core to make a magnet, for he knew that that was the basis of the telephone and of much else in applied electricity.

The man from whom he learned most while in Mifflin was Hiram Sweet, the wagonmaker. But Sweet was more than a wagonmaker. He was, as Kettering said long afterward, "an engineer of such keen ability as to be remarkable. You would no more think of running across such a man in a small town than you would of flying without a flying machine."

Hiram Sweet had invented and built a self-computing cash register which was in daily use in Robinson's drugstore. He had also made an astronomical clock, or perpetual calendar.

"Where did you find out all this?" Kettering asked Sweet.

"I work in this wagon shop ten hours a day," he replied, "from six-thirty in the morning until five-thirty in the after-

As a senior at Ohio State University, with Carl Leibold (left) and Herbert L. Bostater (right). These three men often studied together and they joined in doing their senior thesis.

Bunker Hill schoolhouse where Kettering taught country school in the winter of 1895-96.

Kettering (center of those sitting) with the crew of telephone linemen of which he was foreman in 1900. Standing, second from the right, is Kettering's brother Adam.

Car exhibiting the products of Santa Clara County, California, and containing as a special attraction an X-ray apparatus, which in 1896 Kettering and some of his pupils at Bunker Hill School walked to Loudonville to see.

noon; and when I have no wagonwork to do I work on Sweet's head."

Years afterward, when Kettering had become a noted man, he recalled the days spent in Sweet's wagon shop, "letting him work on my head . . . I learned more from that old wagonmaker than I did in college. . . . The world was so wonderful and he knew so little about it that he hated to sleep."

Toward the end of Kettering's second year at Mifflin his eyesight began to fail him once more, so much so that he had trouble getting through to the end of the term. Nevertheless, during the following summer, his eyes again improved so that when fall came he was able to realize his ambition by going off to The Ohio State University to take a course in engineering.

IV

In September, 1898, Kettering arrived at The Ohio State University in Columbus. A tall, lean-looking young fellow with a shock of black hair, he was twenty-two, about the usual age for seniors, not freshmen. He registered to take the course in electrical engineering. That first term—the academic year was then divided into three terms—he enrolled for chemistry, mathematics, drawing, rhetoric, and German, as well as for cadet service or military drill.

He found a place to live at Mrs. Leonard Young's on Seventh Avenue, about half a mile from his classes. He had to find work, too, for when he entered the university he had very little money. But, by working early and late and living for a while on 35 cents a day, he was able to get along. In his later years at the university, through special skills acquired meanwhile, he made his way without much difficulty. One of those who gave him employment, and by whom he was held in high esteem ever afterward, was John P. Covan, a maintenance supervisor at the university. "I remember, as though it were only yesterday, our various conversations when I was a student many years ago," Kettering wrote to Mr. Covan on the occasion of Covan's eightieth birthday.

What with his financial struggle and discouraging eye difficulties, which again reached a severe stage, Kettering's first year at the university was difficult. But to one of his background and temperament the new and wondrous fields unfolding for him there were so fascinating that, as he remarked in later years, he had just as good a time then as he has ever had in all his life.

In freshman chemistry one of Kettering's laboratory instructors was F. O. Clements. An ambitious young man from Westerville, Ohio, recently graduated from Otterbein College there, Clements was then a teaching fellow and graduate student at the university. The admiration for each other which the two young men developed that year was to bring them together again in later life. It was not many years afterward that, on the recommendation of his former pupil, Clements became chief chemist of the National Cash Register Company, where Kettering was employed. Later still he was to organize a research laboratory for Kettering at his request and then serve for many years as technical director of it.

The keeper of the stockroom to which Kettering went for chemicals needed for his laboratory work in freshman chemistry was R. M. Royer. Royer remembers Kettering as one who drew out many more chemical supplies than did the other students. As the charges for those withdrawals were being punched out on Kettering's student card, Royer would sometimes remonstrate with him, saying that he could not afford to use so much more of those expensive materials than his fellow students found necessary. But later, when out of that uncommon experimental bent of his Kettering had become one of the nation's most creative men, Royer remarked, "I surely get a great kick out of recalling the foolish advice I gave him then."

It was in military drill that Kettering soon met Harry F. Smith, another lanky young man from up in his hilly part of the state, who both in the university and afterward was to be associated with him in several ways. But Kettering did not take kindly to military drill. Soon he failed to show up for the drill period. When Harry Smith saw him next he asked why he had been absent. "I am going to join the University Band," Kettering said. Members of the band were excused from drill. Asked what instrument he was going to play, he replied that he didn't know yet.

Later, when Smith went to Kettering's room, he found him tootling on a clarinet. Kettering explained that the band was short of clarinet players; so, if he played that instrument, they would probably be more patient with him while he was getting the hang of the thing. He had never played a clarinet before, he admitted, but he could read music—all the Ketterings were musical—and he had played the violin.

It was from membership in the band that Kettering got what he said later was one of the important lessons he learned in college. He learned it from the eminent actor, Joseph Jefferson. Jefferson, together with his company, came to the university town to play his famous part of Rip Van Winkle. The leader of the orchestra at the theater was also director of the university band, and he asked Kettering to fill in in the orchestra that evening.

After the show Jefferson invited the members of the orchestra to have supper with him and the company. One of the men asked him how often he had played the part of Rip Van Winkle. The great actor, after consulting a little black book in his pocket, told just how many hundreds of times he had played Rip.

"Don't you get terribly tired doing it so often?" he was asked.

"Yes, I did get tired after a while. But the people wanted Rip. And so I went on playing him. I said to myself, 'It doesn't matter how you feel. Your job is to entertain the audience.' Then I made up my mind that I would try to portray Rip Van Winkle just a little better each time. And that constant effort at improving the part has kept up my interest and enthusiasm."

. . .

In the first two terms of that year, Kettering got along

successfully with his books, in spite of his weak eyes. But by the time the spring term came he could see to read only large print. To get ahead at all he had to rely more and more on the help of others. He would lie on his back on the bed while one of his classmates read the day's assignments aloud.

Recalling those events in later life, he made the remark that he could always tell how much studying he had done the evening before by how hoarse his roommate was in the morning. At the time, there was little humor in the situation, however.

In spite of his bad eyesight, he nevertheless succeeded that first year in getting a Merit grade—the highest mark given—in 70 per cent of the hours taken. Also, because he could read less and less, he learned more and more to picture things in his mind. This capacity was valuable to him in later life. Without imagination, he said once, you can't get anywhere. He even remarked that by such mental digestion of new facts "you can know three times as much as you know now without learning any more."

Thus, thanks in large part to the generous aid of his fellows, he got through that first year. And after a summer at home on the farm he returned to the university in the fall of 1899 for his sophomore year. But the condition of his eyes then went from bad to worse. Not only could he not see to study, but also the headaches which plagued him grew more and more violent. He became sick, and his eyes failed him so completely that he simply had to leave the university.

At that point he was a disheartened young man. Leaving for home, he said to Mrs. Young, his landlady and sympathetic friend, "If my eyes won't let me finish my schooling, I hope the train runs off the track and kills me."

V

Some time after Kettering got home that fall he felt able to go to Mifflin to see his friends, druggist John Robinson and wagonmaker Hiram Sweet. Now it happened that just then a gang of men setting poles for a telephone line were working through the village of Mifflin. Hoping that outside work of that kind would be good for him, Kettering asked the foreman for a job and was put to work immediately.

The line crew he thus joined was working for the Star Telephone Company of Ashland, a county seat of about 4,000 population situated a few miles north of Mifflin. In impulsively beginning that telephone work, Kettering entered upon a course of events that was to have a large influence in directing his future career.

He began by digging holes for telephone poles but soon became foreman of the line gang. Outdoor work put little strain on his eyes and his vision and general health improved rapidly. Soon he was full of energy and enthusiasm. To put up forty-five crossarms on telephone poles was considered a good day's work for two men. But one day, just to see what they could do, he and A. D. (Mont) George, a fellow worker who became Kettering's lifelong friend, put up ninety crossarms.

So fast did Kettering work sometimes that he did not always take time to fasten his safety belt when working at the top of a pole. And once, when the bite of one of his climbing spikes tore out, he went tumbling down. Only the chance that in his fall he struck a wire saved him from what might have been serious injury.

34

Those men who worked on the line crew of the telephone company were tough and rugged. They were not always easy to get along with, but Kettering did get along with them. They admired him for his friendliness and his capabilities. He was slender, but wiry and strong. Not for nothing had he spent his younger years doing farm work. He could hold an iron crowbar out at arm's length, a feat by which the men used to demonstrate their strength.

From association with those telephone men Kettering got his unusual expressiveness in swearing. He came to have the same eloquence in that respect as Mark Twain or Thomas A. Edison. In afteryears, when he was chosen as the first president of the Thomas A. Edison Foundation, he made the quip that he supposed he was picked for that job because he was the only man who could swear the way Edison did. But in his earlier life he was not given to swearing. He picked it up in the telephone years and used it to put pungency into what he said, particularly in the intense and sometimes rough-and-tumble situations of his middle life.

For the toilsome job of setting telephone poles men were sometimes hard to get, especially in summer when it was hot. Kettering himself, though, liked heat better than cold. "The way to make a Christian out of me," he said once, "would not be to threaten heat in the life hereafter but to freeze me in a cake of ice."

One hot day, as the men were sitting in the shade eating their lunches, a tramp happened by and asked for a bite to eat. Kettering took the hobo into a restaurant near by and filled him up. Afterward he asked him, "How would you like to have a good job so you could always have plenty to eat?"

Even out of his hobo sense of decency the fellow thought he ought to pretend to work a little for the good meal he had just had. So Kettering gave him some tools, and left

35

him. Returning soon afterward, he found the man, with hands already blistered and with sweat streaming down his face, actually trying to dig a hole. And what a hole it was! The ground there was underlaid with a hardpan of shale, and the hole he had dug was just a jagged depression.

Meaning to encourage the inexperienced digger, Kettering said, "Come with me and let me show you what a nice hole looks like." He led him over to one of those dug by Joe, the best hole-digger in the gang. It was smooth and round, with walls perfectly perpendicular.

Kettering then began to dig one himself, talking meanwhile in this vein: "It's fun to dig a hole. And the rounder you dig it and the straighter you dig it the more fun it is. It's fun to see how nearly perpendicular and smooth you can make the sides of the hole." Soon the man actually became interested and wanted to try his hand at the job again.

The result was that he stayed and worked on and on. He became not only the best hole-digger they had ever had— better even than Joe—but after a time he was made foreman of the line gang. And later, when Kettering came that way, the ex-hobo said to him: "You were the first person ever to tell me that work could be fun. If only years ago someone had taught me how much fun it is to work, when a fellow tries to do *good* work, I would never have become the bum I was."

Soon Kettering was asked whether he could install a telephone exchange. Certainly, he could—although in truth he knew mighty little about it. But the obstacle of not knowing how never kept him from undertaking anything he thought needed to be done. "It is a fundamental rule with me," he said once, "that if I want to do something I start, whether I know how or not. . . . As a rule you can find that out by trying."

He sent for a book, *American Telephone Practice,* by Kempster B. Miller of the Kellogg Switchboard and Supply Company, published that same year. With its clear diagrams and plain explanations, that book proved to be just what he needed to supplement the little he already knew and the knowledge he acquired as he went along. Thus he was able to install the exchange.

It was while installing another exchange that Kettering first talked to Olive Williams. Mont George, who knew Olive, was helping him install an exchange at West Salem, a town not far from Ashland, and that demanded a certain amount of test calling. Having called up Olive Williams that day, Mont said while talking to her: "I've got a fellow here, Charlie Kettering, who is a good talker." He had previously told Kettering that Olive Williams was mighty quick on the comeback. The kidding conversation between Charlie Kettering and Olive Williams that day came under the head of "testing," but it was the beginning of a lifelong romance.

In his waggish way Kettering had told Harry Smith that he was going to marry a redheaded girl who could play the piano. Olive Williams—they called her Ollie at home—did not have red hair but she could play the piano and on Sundays played the pipe organ in one of Ashland's churches.

Olive's brother, Ralph D. Williams, remembers that on one of Kettering's calls at the Williams home he brought with him a telephone transmitter, mounted it behind Olive's piano, and connected it into the telephone circuit so that the music from the piano could be heard on the line. Ralph remembers also that at slack times the telephone operators in Cleveland used to ring the Williams home and ask Olive to play for them. Sometimes they even put subscribers on the line to hear Olive Williams play the piano down in Ashland.

. . .

The most notable work Kettering did for the Star Telephone Company was to install in the exchange at Ashland a central, or common, battery system. At that time a country telephone consisted universally of a wooden box containing its own dry-cell batteries and a magneto with a hand crank for ringing. On such a party line each subscriber had an assigned code of long and short rings, for all the telephones on the line rang at once. And of course at every call receivers came down all along the line and people listened in on the conversation that followed. It was to correct that situation by making each telephone ring independently and also to give better service and reduce operating costs that Kettering wanted to install a central battery system.

But, as those country telephone lines extended fifteen miles or more from town, he was told that on such a long line of iron wire the resistance was far too great for a central battery system to be practical. The resistance of iron wire is five times that of the copper wire used in town lines. All the same, he set up experiments to find out what could be done to make such a system work successfully. He constructed at headquarters a pilot system and worked on it for long hours, sometimes until past midnight.

He developed relays and impedance coils to take the resistance off the line, or to match the resistance inside the exchange with that on the outside. He increased the number of batteries in the current source, and he made many other adjustments until he was sure he had the right combination of factors.

Then he undertook the installation of the system, though he found that no one would furnish the necessary relays and impedance coils with proper characteristics. So he unwound coils of a kind that could be purchased and then rewound them in the form needed. For doing that job he made use of his boyhood experience with his mother's sewing machine by winding the coils on the bobbin winder of an old sewing machine procured for the purpose.

When the new central battery system was put into service it worked just as his experiments had predicted it would, and everyone was pleased. That is, it worked well for a while. And then a baffling difficulty developed. The trouble was so serious and so perplexing that telephone people wanted to throw out the new system and go back to the old. "No," said Kettering; "we've got to find the cause of this trouble."

The difficulty was that almost every afternoon the line would go out of commission altogether. The minute the failure appeared, servicemen set out posthaste in search of its source. But before they could get far in their horse-drawn vehicle the trouble always disappeared.

Then Kettering took over. He went out to the halfway point on the line and waited for the trouble to appear. It came just as expected, and his test showed that its location was still farther out on the line. At the second telephone inspected he found it.

In that house there was an old man who took a nap every afternoon. Before lying down he hung his steel-rimmed spectacles by their bows in the loops of wire at the two exposed binding posts of the telephone. That put a metal short across the line and caused the system to be out of service until he took his spectacles down.

This resolute attitude of not accepting defeat has saved Kettering from failure on many of his important endeavors. "If an experiment fails," he would say, "then you ought to be careful to find out just why it failed, because the failure may not have had anything to do with the reasonableness of the principle."

He has also said: "Every great improvement . . . has come after repeated failures. . . . Virtually nothing comes out

39

right the first time. Failures, repeated failures, are finger posts on the road to achievement."

But all that work was fun for Kettering. It was precisely the kind of pursuit which throughout his life has given him his greatest enjoyment.

Still, he wanted to complete his course at the university. That desire was intensified in the second summer of his telephone work by experiments he was making on lightning arresters. As he expressed it long afterward, "I began to realize that we didn't know anything about this thing and I thought maybe I had better go back to school and find out something about it."

So in the fall of 1901, after nearly two years as a telephone man, he returned to Ohio State to see if now his eyes would let him go ahead with his engineering course. But he expected to come back to Ashland during vacations and in the summertime to continue working for the telephone company—and also to be near Olive Williams.

VI

When, in 1901, Kettering went back to Ohio State to begin once more his sophomore year, he was past twenty-five. Again he lived at Mrs. Leonard Young's on Seventh Avenue, four blocks from the edge of the campus. Two other young men living there, Herbert L. Bostater and Carl P. Leibold, were in his class taking electrical engineering also.

Those three men often studied together, and later they joined in doing their senior thesis as well. Continuing to save his eyes, Kettering would often listen to the other men reading the daily assignments aloud, just as he had been forced to do in the latter part of his freshman year. As Leibold remembered it, he and Bostater did the reading and Ket— as they called him for short—did the thinking.

Because Kettering was older than the other students and because he had a wider background of experience, he did think out problems more deeply and more thoroughly. He was interested in principles and fundamentals, not in committing something to memory. In the course on boilers and steam engines, Professor William T. Magruder, his exacting teacher in mechanical engineering, required students to memorize certain details, such as the grate area and stack height needed for generating a given amount of steam. But such details had little interest for Kettering. He tried to fill his mind not with figures but with understanding. Nevertheless, he was one of those to whom Professor Magruder gave his highest mark for the course, a Merit grade.

That Kettering did understand the problem of making steam he soon demonstrated in an interesting way. A small factory in Ashland had installed a new boiler. But they could not keep the steam pressure up. So, for the winter vacation, Kettering went to that plant to see if he could do anything to help.

He noticed at once that it was hard to open the door of the boiler room. Then, when he had stepped inside, the door slammed shut behind him. That gave him the clue to the trouble. The furnace fire was so starved for air that it sucked the door shut. So he opened some windows. Whereupon the steam pressure soon went up to what it ought to have been.

Kettering's difficulty with his eyes was by then merely one which would not let him do close work. Although it did not prevent him from seeing well otherwise, it would not let him take the practice part of the courses in engineering drawing, which were a requirement for graduation. The faculty considered the matter and reluctantly decided to allow him to confine his work in drawing to the lectures and recitations; but he must take some other suitable courses to compensate for the omission, they said. So Professor Thomas E. French, head of engineering drawing and a man who became one of Kettering's greatest admirers, called him in to tell him what the faculty had decided. And Professor French warned him that he better get a Merit grade in whatever substitute subjects he took.

Since Kettering had liked chemistry so much in his freshman year, he chose first to take quantitative analysis, which was chiefly laboratory work. That second-year course in chemistry he took under Professor C. W. Foulk. Professor Foulk was a colorful teacher who soon observed that he had in his class a quite unusual student. He remembers that Kettering seldom did things in strict accordance with the book. Nevertheless, he did them well. Whenever he set up a piece of analytical apparatus, it differed in some respects from the conventional as called for by the directions. But always his apparatus fulfilled its purpose in good style; and, as Professor Foulk said, he never saw any need to ask him to change what he had done.

During his junior year Kettering took also an advanced course in chemistry, and later an additional course in physics. In the advanced chemistry course his teacher was the professor of physical chemistry, William E. Henderson. The important theory of ionization, or electrolytic dissociation in solutions of electrolytes, was new then. It was natural that to Kettering, with his interest in everything electrical, that theory should have been one of the most fascinating in all chemistry, and he remembers with appreciation the thorough manner in which Professor Henderson covered it. For what Kettering was to do in later years those extra courses in science were far more important preparation than the work on the drawing board, which his weak eyes caused him to miss and which omission seemed so regrettable to his professors of engineering.

Mathematics was another subject for which Kettering had a special liking. In class he was so evidently interested that one of his teachers, Professor James E. Boyd, said that when lecturing he sometimes found himself talking to Kettering instead of to the group in general. Because of Kettering's proficiency in the field of mathematics, Professor Boyd suggested to him that he go further in his study of the subject and make a major of it. But another of Kettering's mathematics teachers, Professor R. D. Bohannon, who had a better understanding of him and his capabilities, advised him more wisely. Gentleman of the old school, dog fancier, and horseman, who occasionally came to class accompanied by one of his collie dogs and wearing his red riding coat, Professor Bohannon was an excellent teacher who stood especially high in Kettering's esteem. When Professor Bohannon heard of the advice his colleague, Professor Boyd, had given, he said to Kettering: "Don't you do it. Mathematics cannot give you what you want. It will be better for you to stick to your experiments."

Kettering's interest in new knowledge went further than his college books. It had been only a few years before he was a student at the university that Charles P. Steinmetz, the great experimenter and pioneer in the understanding of things electrical, published his historic work on alternating current phenomena. That was a complicated treatise full of differential equations and involved mathematics. Meeting Harry Smith on the campus one day, Kettering told him that he had been studying Steinmetz's work and that he had succeeded in reducing what the author had said to quite simple terms. Whereupon he pulled out of his pocket an envelope on which he had written the electrical analogies of the elements of mass, elasticity, velocity, inertia, etc. Right there, he said, is all that Steinmetz's book is about. To Carl Leibold, too, Kettering said he wanted to understand alternating current electricity well enough to be able to talk to Steinmetz in his own language.

"Things don't need to be complicated," he said later. "Personally, I believe that you can simplify anything you understand." He even talked about writing a little book on the correlation and simplification of knowledge in the different fields of science by expressing the fundamental laws or concepts of all of them in equivalent terms. He never got around to doing that, but he often remarked that anything is "scientific" when you don't understand it. As soon as you do, it's not scientific any more.

All through his university course Kettering had to continue to work to cover his expenses. But he gradually shifted to jobs based upon the knowledge he was acquiring. Once there was trouble in a telephone cable near Columbus,

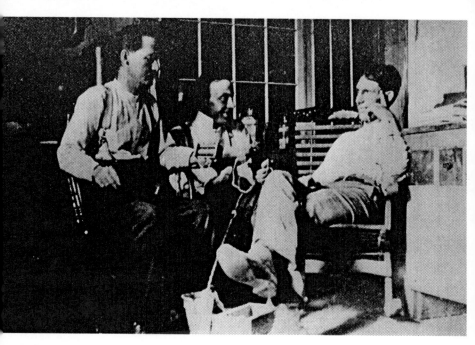

With druggist John Robinson and a fellow school teacher, George Gruenwald, in Robinson's drug store at Mifflin, Ohio. Here the three men (Kettering at right) made experiments in elementary chemistry and electricity.

Interior of the Deeds barn about 1910 when experimentation on battery ignition was in progress. At the left, Robert Walton; next, W. P. Anderson; at the drill press, right, W. A. Chryst.

The Deeds barn at 319 Central Avenue, Dayton, Ohio. In this building Kettering did his historic work on the development of battery ignition and the automobile self-starter.

In the laboratory of "Inventions 3" at the National Cash Register Company with W. A. Chryst (left). On the table in the foreground is a cash register fitted with an early model of the OK Charge Phone, Kettering's first development at NCR.

which the trouble shooters of the telephone company had not been able to locate. The company turned to the university with an urgent plea for assistance. Because of Kettering's experience with telephones, he was asked to see what he could do to help. He was glad to accept, for he wanted to try a scheme he had worked out in the physics laboratory for just such a situation.

Out on the line he set up the instruments he had borrowed from the Department of Electrical Engineering at the university and waited patiently until past midnight for the temperatures in the cable to equalize. Then he carefully took several measurements of electrical resistance from each of two locations on the line a considerable distance apart and on either side of the fault. By means of his system he spotted the trouble within a short section of the cable, in the middle of which was a splice.

The telephone people doubted that the trouble was in that splice, for it had just been made by one of their best cable splicers. But Kettering took his knife and at the bottom lifted the edge of the lead sheathing around the splice. And, sure enough, out came a telltale trickle of water. Then with the experience he had gained at Ashland he made a new splice, and the trouble was gone.

As payment for his night's work he would take only $125, although he was offered more. That sum was enough for one night's work, he said. Anyway, it was enough to cover about a third of his yearly expenses at the university.

A thesis based upon some investigation was required for graduation from the College of Engineering. In Kettering's case, the senior thesis related of course to the telephone, the principal subject of his interest at the time. His fellow students, Bostater and Leibold, joined with him in the experimentation and in the writing of the thesis. They chose as their title, "A Study of the Design of Certain Types of Telephone Apparatus."

In telephone circuits, the investigators wrote, "the matter of current volume and secondary voltage has been almost entirely a matter of conjecture." The measurement of such quantities was "extremely difficult," for "the currents and voltage used in telephony are alternating and of a very complex nature so small in value that all ordinary types of AC instruments are insensible to their effect."

But, by means of instruments and techniques which they devised, the three student investigators were able to show that currents and voltages in telephone circuits could be measured accurately and the results used to great advantage in the design of telephone apparatus. Their thesis would have done credit to anyone in the graduate school.

Before the end of Kettering's senior year a letter came to the university asking for a young man with an inventive turn of mind and a good knowledge of electricity to join the inventions staff of the National Cash Register Company at Dayton, Ohio. The letter was written by E. A. Deeds, a young executive of the company, and was addressed to Professor A. D. Cole of the Department of Physics.

Professor Cole could think of no one better qualified for that job than Kettering, who was by then a student assistant in the department. But Kettering was interested primarily in getting back into the telephone business. However, Professor Cole, with his favorable knowledge of Deeds, who was a former student of his, persuaded Kettering to go to Dayton and see Deeds anyway. The outcome was that he did accept a job at the National Cash Register Company.

Some of his friends thought though that he was throwing away his chance for success. At that time every graduate in electrical engineering who amounted to anything went as a matter of course into the established electrical companies, such as General Electric, Westinghouse, or Bell Telephone. But what Kettering's fellow students may not have known was that he was to begin work at a salary of $50 a week, whereas the graduates in electrical engineering who went to the electrical companies started as apprentices at 17 or 18 cents an hour, not one-fourth of what he was to get.

And so at last, nearly six years after Kettering had first entered the university, graduation time came. He was then almost twenty-eight years old. His father and mother came down for Commencement, and Olive Williams, too.

There is a legend that when he got his diploma he threw it in the wastebasket. The truth is that he prized it highly and still has it. But he did not want the possession of a diploma to stop him from learning.

When, just twenty-five years after his graduation, he was the first alumnus of Ohio State to speak at Commencement, he ended his address to the graduating class as follows:

"There are two things, there are three things, which if you get your point of view right, you will have no trouble with. The first is that you are going to be a servant to somebody or something. . . . The next is that to be a good servant implies two things, willingness to work and willingness to learn, because no one of us knows very much. . . . And if, when you pack your bag for this eventful journey . . . you pack egotism and selfishness and all that sort of thing down in the bottom of the bag, and if you lay your servant's uniform on top, the passports will not have to be opened, and they will pass you through the line."

Although his originality and individualism had sometimes clashed with the rigid academic system at Ohio State, Kettering left in June, 1904, with deep gratitude for what the

47

university and its faculty had done for him. And ever since he has done whatever he could to repay his indebtedness.

When the faculty had been questioning whether to let him go through his course without engineering drawing, Professor Bohannon made the astute observation that Kettering was likely to do more for the university than the university could do for him. And he has made that prediction come true. For one thing, he is in his fourth seven-year term as a trustee of the university, having already served in that capacity for twenty-seven years.

PART II
Middle Years
1905–1919

VII

IT WAS ON THE FIRST DAY of July, 1904, that Kettering entered what he said later was his graduate school. This was the inventions staff of the National Cash Register Company at Dayton, Ohio, which for short was called NCR. In actuality, NCR was only Kettering's first graduate school; for in every activity of his future career he continued his search for knowledge.

The president of NCR was John H. Patterson, a genius of a man, sandy-haired farm boy and ex-coal dealer, who, at the age of forty, had organized the company around a purchased invention, an embryonic cash register. Patterson was a business showman and pioneer in modern methods of advertising and selling. Through his originality and prodigious drive, together with the aid of the many capable men he gathered around him, he had built the concern into one of the best in the nation. He had a special knack of picking good men and was said to have conducted "the greatest business university in America." Through the intensity of his program, he was said also to have forced his men "either to the front or out the back door."

One of the best men in Patterson's "business university" was the young executive E. A. Deeds who was responsible for bringing Kettering into the concern. Deeds was only two years older than Kettering, and soon the two young men came to hold each other in high esteem. Later they were to unite their talents: Kettering's independent inventiveness and Deeds's business sagacity.

At the time Kettering joined NCR he and Deeds were the

only men with technical training at the college level on the staff of the concern. The feeling then was that the business needed "practical" men, not "those book-learnin' guys."

When Kettering went to NCR he was by no means the usual new college graduate. Almost twenty-eight, he was already a self-taught but experienced experimenter. He had also the enthusiasm, the intensity of interest, and the boundless energy essential to success in the tough business of developing new products.

Soon after Kettering arrived at NCR he was put in charge of the development department called Inventions 3, one of a number of departments. He was particularly fortunate in the make-up of the group around him. The man whom Deeds designated as Kettering's first assistant was W. A. (Bill) Chryst, who had been a designer in one of the other inventions departments. That choice turned out to be fortunate, for Bill Chryst became the perfect complement to CF, as they came to call him.

CF was essentially an idea man, an originator or trail blazer. Usually he was so bubbling over with ideas that, although he was a doer as well as a dreamer, he did not always have the time nor the inclination to work out all the practical details. For his ideas to be fully successful, someone was needed to see that what was necessary to make them work practically was done. For many years, both at NCR and later, Bill Chryst—capable, sincere, and sound in judgment—was that man.

The first job Kettering did at NCR was not to put an electric drive on the cash register but to develop what came to be called the O.K. Charge Phone. It was difficult then to sell cash registers to department stores because of their need to have also a means of handling credit sales. Thus many department stores preferred the old system of handling both cash and credits at a central point.

By combining the telephone with the cash register and by building into the system also a magnetic stamping device operated from the central credit department for authorizing charge sales at the point of selling, Kettering developed the O.K. Charge Phone. It corrected a major deficiency of the cash register for department store use. He did it all within a few months.

The work on the O.K. Charge Phone brought Kettering into association with R. H. Grant, an outstanding salesman and member of the NCR sales force. Later Grant was to be sales manager and then general manager of one of the concerns set up by Kettering and Deeds, and later still vice-president of sales for General Motors.

Kettering's contact with Grant quickened the interest in salesmanship and in the viewpoint of the customer which he already had. He took the course in salesmanship offered by NCR in evenings, in what was called the Owl Class, and which had for its motto the single word "Dig."

Recalling his years at NCR, Kettering said, "I didn't hang around much with other inventors or the executive fellows. I lived with the sales gang. They had some real notion of what people wanted." And sensitivity to what people want has all through his life been a marked characteristic. "Remember," he said once, "that you and I get no place in the world except in proportion as we serve the fellow who pays for our dinner."

He set out next to substitute an electric drive for the tiresome hand crank on the cash register, two turns of which had to be made to ring up each sale, even if only five cents in amount. This was the job for which he had been hired. Putting an electric drive on the cash register was not so simple as on a sewing machine, for example. Not only did the motor have to be small and inconspicuous to satisfy the critical eye of President Patterson. The cash register, being a counting mechanism, had also to be stopped at exactly the right point. To make that possible, Kettering developed a different kind of motor, one with extra high turning power for its size and a clutch for engaging the mechanism of the cash register and then releasing it at just the right time. His motor need not conform to the accepted practice for electric motors, he knew, for it had to put forth only a momentary burst of power.

His new clutch was called an overrunning clutch, and some years later he used it again, and also the principle of a small motor with high torque effort, in his electric self-starter for the automobile. "More than once," he remarked, "we have seen research accomplishments fit together, like the words of a crossword puzzle, to aid us in solving other problems."

Many difficulties had to be overcome before the motorized cash register was successful. But gradually they were solved, and the new register opened wide the market for cash registers which before had begun to close in dangerously.

On August 1, 1905, in the midst of the difficulties of finding how to make the electric motor on the cash register operate on alternating current as well as direct, Charlie Kettering and Olive Williams were married. The wedding took place at the home of Olive's parents, Mr. and Mrs. Alonzo Williams, in Ashland, Ohio.

After the wedding, which was early in the day, Olive's brother, Ralph D. Williams, drove the couple the fourteen miles to Mansfield, Ohio, in a surrey. There they took the train for Detroit as the first stop on their wedding trip.

They changed trains at Crestline, Ohio. While waiting there, Kettering saw a man cranking and cranking the engine of his automobile in an unsuccessful attempt to start it. Cranking an automobile had to be done by hand, of course.

So Kettering walked over to see whether he might be of any help. He found the ignition system out of order. And, being an old telephone man, he knew how to fix it.

In appreciation for his help, the owner, a doctor in the town, invited the two of them to take a ride with him in his car. And so on their wedding day Charlie and Olive Kettering rode through the streets of Crestline on what was their first automobile ride. Mrs. Kettering remembered that the doctor's car was one of those early models in which the rear seat faced backwards.

In Detroit the newlyweds stayed at the original Cadillac Hotel at Michigan Avenue and Washington Boulevard. Afterward they went on to Niagara Falls and other places. Years later, in a suite on the twenty-second floor of the successor to the old Cadillac Hotel, the Book-Cadillac (now the Sheraton-Cadillac), they were to live for about half of their married life.

While on that wedding trip Kettering wrote a long letter to Bill Chryst. It was devoted mostly to schemes he had worked up meanwhile and which he thought would make the alternating current motor just as good for powering the cash register as his direct current motor had proved to be. At the end he wrote that he had taken some good pictures of Niagara Falls.

When the Ketterings got to Dayton, Charlie immediately plunged again into the problems at NCR. Mrs. Kettering became the capable manager of the household. She handled the family funds and saw to it that some portion of Kettering's earnings was saved.

"As an inventor, I have been very lucky in having had some of the best managers in the country," Kettering said once. Foremost among the persons he meant was Mrs. Kettering. "She was the general manager, and a perfect supplement to an absent-minded inventor."

The most important way in which Mrs. Kettering served as the "perfect supplement" was in understanding him for the uncommon man he was and in taking up the job of looking after his welfare in every way she could. She bought his clothes. And, because of his unconcern about clothes, she made it a rule to see that he was well dressed when he left home in the morning. If she was away from home for any considerable time, Kettering's associates could tell from the clothes he wore just when she got back. By her efforts she gradually got him to pay more attention to his appearance, so that in time he even became a well-dressed man. But all his life it has been a habit of his not to let the clothes he is wearing interfere with what he thinks needs to be done at the time.

In keeping her husband fitted with proper clothes, Mrs. Kettering had particular trouble with hats, for she could not get him to the store to try one on. And he complained that the hats she bought for him did not fit his head. So he always preferred an old hat to a new one. Some he persisted in wearing until they were so old and shapeless that, as Mrs. Kettering told him, they were disgraceful.

Once when Ivan Teetor drove Kettering to the hospital to see Mrs. Kettering, he was wearing an old and pretty badly battered hat. As Kettering was going up the steps of the hospital, he turned, came back to the car, and said: "I am going to leave my hat here." And Teetor knew that it was out of regard for the feelings of Mrs. Kettering that he did it.

It was during the years at NCR, on April 20, 1908, that the only child of the Ketterings was born. He was named Eugene Williams, but came to be called Gene for short. As will be told later, Gene grew up to follow in the footsteps of his father.

No sooner had Kettering returned from his wedding trip than the heads of NCR decided that, to meet certain competition, they needed a very simple cash register that could be sold at a low price. And it was needed, they thought, in a great hurry. To meet that demand, Kettering and his assistants worked, ate, and slept the new register for many weeks. The scheme they evolved was for a spring-powered register in which the tension of the spring would be reset each time by the force exerted in closing the drawer.

But there was opposition from some men in the company to using a spring for actuation. Springs are not dependable, they said, and will not stand up. To silence one objector, Kettering used some of the wile he can always summon. He happened to know that that man was a watch fancier who usually had more than one watch on his person. So he asked the objector if he had a watch.

Yes, he had. In fact, he had two of them in his pocket just then.

"Do those watches of yours keep good time?"

"Why, certainly. And I've had this one for twenty years, too," he said with pride as he took one of the watches out of his pocket.

"Let me see your watch a moment," said Kettering. "I want to find out what makes it go." The man's objections to springs vanished in the big laugh that went up.

Pressure for development of the drawer-operated register was made stronger by the circumstance that President Patterson was soon to leave on a trip to Europe. Kettering was asked whether he thought the development could be finished before the date of his departure. Yes, he thought it could.

"We ought really to have the job completed sooner," said Patterson. So he directed that Kettering be given more help. "Give him twice as many men," he said, "so he can finish it up in half the time."

At that, Kettering protested that he could not use so many helpers to advantage.

"Why can't you?" Patterson asked. "If ten men can dig a rod of ditch in an hour, then surely twenty men can dig two rods."

"This is more a job of hatching eggs than digging ditches, Mr. Patterson," was the reply. "Do you think that if two hens were put on a nest a setting of eggs could be hatched out in less than three weeks?"

Kettering's intensity of interest in getting work done was put into this saying: "I have always told my gang that I don't want any fellow that has a job working for me, but I do want some fellow whom the job has. In other words, I want the job to get the fellow, not the fellow to get the job."

Because of the enthusiastic drive that Kettering and his assistants put behind it, the new register—the first low-cost printing cash register—was completed in record time. "Never before, nor since, in the long history of this company," said an account of the major developments at NCR written thirty years later, "has a comparable job been done in so short a time."

It was a simple register, said Kettering. "We didn't have time to make it complicated."

Kettering was not too engrossed in his work to have fun, however. It was a custom of President Patterson's to provide entertainment for his employees and their families. One of these was a home talent show. Kettering was a crack shot and had been practicing marksmanship at noontime with Bill Schutte, one of the sales force, Bill Chryst, and others. So it was suggested that he and Schutte enter the home talent show with a shooting act, and they agreed to do it.

They decided to "shoot out" candles on the stage from a position at the front of the balcony. After shooting out a row of candles with unerring effectiveness, it was announced that they would "split" a bullet on a knife blade placed vertically edge forward in front of the row of candles—and do it in such precise fashion that the fragments would put out the two end candles at the same time. And, after one or two unsuccessful shots to heighten the effect, they performed the feat just as promised.

Their act was a sensation. A scout from a vaudeville chain tried to sign up the marksmen for a tour of his circuit. But to the two dead shots it was all in fun. The whole thing was faked, said Kettering afterward. Each candle sat on a black box the side of which was part of a bellows. They merely shot at the bellows and a quick puff of air from it blew out the candle.

Once, too, there were scare stories of a monster snake having been seen by different people in the vicinity of Dayton. As a joke, Kettering and Chryst fell in with the rumor. They set out to make some pictures which, because "the camera does not lie," would be photographic "proof" of the existence of that huge snake. They built a miniature rail fence out of little sticks only a few inches long. Then they caught a little garter snake, posed it on that tiny fence, and photographed it there in close-up to give an illusion of great size. Afterward the two wags exhibited that photograph as proof positive that the huge and frightening snake that people were talking about really did exist.

Soon came a demand for an accounting machine that could be used by banks, one having multiple counters and incorporating a means of subtracting as well as adding. How to do that subtraction was the puzzle that had to be solved.

One day Deeds happened to show Kettering a drawing of an automobile auxiliary in which he was interested. Part of that device was a differential like that in the rear axle of an automobile. At sight of that differential Kettering's eyes brightened. It gave him an inkling of how he might make the counting wheels of his bank machine go either forward to add or backward to subtract, and to do either without changing the direction of the drive.

Next morning, while he was shaving, the conception came to him of just how he could fit the principle of the differential gear into the register to subtract or add at will. He hurried to the laboratory, and by ten o'clock that night he and Chryst had the embryo scheme in operation for the first time.

After many months of intensive development, the men came up with an accounting machine based on a new and major principle. And that new machine had a marvelously beneficial effect upon business at NCR. It was for many years the backbone of the concern's sales. In a later account of major developments at NCR published by the company it was said that this development was "an outstanding illustration of ability to look into the future and to plan adequately for the coming years."

It was while the development of the accounting machine was in progress, or before it had been fully finished, that Kettering decided to end his work at NCR. He resigned to develop on his own account another idea born in his fertile brain—an improved ignition system for automobiles. So in the fall of 1909 his productive career there came to a close.

In only a little more than five years at NCR, Kettering had made four major contributions to the concern, not to mention many minor ones. He had done away with the hand crank of the cash register, he had developed the O.K. Charge Phone and a simple low-cost printing register, and he had originated an accounting or bank machine. These four developments of his served for many years as the principal products of the company.

VIII

For august 10, 1908, W. A. Chryst made this entry in his little diary: "CFK full of auto ignition project." On that date Kettering was still working at NCR and was right in the midst of one of his major endeavors, the development of the multiple-counter bank machine. All the same, there was room in his versatile mind for consideration of this new problem, how to improve ignition in the automobile engine.

It was Earl Howard who stirred Kettering's interest in that problem. Howard had been secretary to E. A. Deeds but had gone off to Detroit, where he had become assistant sales manager of the Cadillac Motor Car Company. Visiting in Dayton one Sunday, Howard told Kettering that at Cadillac they were not satisfied with the automobile ignition systems of that time and asked him if he couldn't think up a solution for the difficulty.

To one of Kettering's intense interest in electricity and magnetism, that suggestion was like giving an electric train to a boy—or to his father. He couldn't wait to start experimenting. Kettering set up some pieces of apparatus at home, he recalled, and soon arrived at the conclusion that it was possible to make a more satisfactory ignition system.

Two types of electric ignition were in use on automobile engines then, magneto and battery. Both were usually employed on the same automobile with means for switching from one to the other. But neither was completely satisfactory. It was thought that battery ignition was not good at high engine speed, and magneto ignition was given to missing and stalling at low engine speeds. Many a driver was exasperated when his engine stopped in traffic or elsewhere

61

on that account. In battery ignition, dry cells were used as a source of current, not the higher capacity wet batteries of the present. A set of dry cells would sometimes last no more than 200 miles.

Making use of his knowledge of magnetism, and especially of his familiarity with the relay gained in his telephone experience, Kettering devised a battery ignition circuit contaning a holding coil, which he called an ignition relay. This gave—instead of the customary shower of sparks, so unreliable and so wasteful of batteries—just one "fat" spark for each contact of the timer or distributor, thereby extending by tenfold the life of the dry cells used.

A place to experiment was soon set up in the barn at the rear of the Deeds home, 319 Central Avenue, for Deeds, too, had become interested in the ignition endeavor. There Kettering, assisted by Chryst and others, spent evenings and weekends at the problem of developing his new scheme for an ignition system into one that would be simple, inexpensive to make, and thoroughly reliable in operation. The entries in Chryst's diary then began to be devoted in large part to the night work going on in the Deeds barn. "Working on CF's ignition stuff until 10:30" was a typical entry.

To provide the machine tools the men needed in that experimental work, Mrs. Kettering took out of their savings $1,500, nearly the total amount. With that money Kettering bought a lathe and a milling machine to add to the meager equipment in their little shop. This was only the beginning of Mrs. Kettering's efforts to help her husband in his independent inventive endeavors. Often when the men were working late in the barn she would bring them coffee and an evening snack. Remembering the loyal support she gave him during that trying period and afterward, Kettering said of her, "She was a great help in those early struggles, for she never got discouraged."

It was in the upper story of the barn, in the space that had been the hayloft when horses were kept there, that most of the work was done. And how insufferably hot it was up there under that roof on some summer nights! The stairway to the hayloft was narrow and winding, but Kettering dashed up and down it many times in the course of an evening, from his experimental car on the first floor to the loft where the parts were being formed. He had bought a Cadillac roadster to use as a guinea pig on which to try out the new ignition system and the changes being made in it.

While the work in the barn was in progress, Deeds was writing letters to Henry M. Leland, president of Cadillac, trying to interest him in the new ignition system. After Kettering had made a trip or two to Detroit to see the Cadillac people, there came one day a telegram from Leland. He was sending his chief engineer, E. E. Sweet, down to Dayton that night, the telegram said, to see just what they had.

Kettering and Deeds met Sweet at the train in the morning, got him into their test car and went for a long demonstration drive over the hill roads to the south of Dayton. With Sweet driving, the new ignition system performed perfectly all day. Try as he would, Sweet could not make the engine misbehave or miss even once. He came back from that test with an excellent impression of the reliability of the system.

After Sweet had been delivered to the train to Detroit, Kettering and Deeds returned to the test car only to find that, although they cranked the engine patiently, it simply wouldn't start. After much searching for the difficulty, Kettering found that one of the wires in the ignition system had broken its connection. What would have been the effect if that had happened during the time Sweet was driving the car they did not dare to think.

After some further negotiations between Dayton and Detroit, Deeds and Kettering were called up to Detroit by Henry Leland, where a contract to furnish Cadillac 8,000 of the battery ignition sets was quickly worked out and signed.

This was really more than the two men had contemplated. They were thinking only of becoming originators of new products, not manufacturers of anything. The name they had given their little organization was an indication of that, the Dayton Engineering Laboratories Company. Bill Chryst had suggested that particular wording to make the initials spell "Delco," and that was the name by which the concern came to be known.

Deeds recalled that, as with their heads swimming they left Cadillac that exciting July day in 1909, Kettering had the newly signed contract for 8,000 ignition sets in his pocket. "Here," he said to Deeds, "you take it; I don't want it."

"I don't want it either," Deeds replied.

They did not at first know just how they were going to get the ignition sets made. But, in view of their determination not to become a manufacturing concern, they turned to J. B. Edwards, president of the Kellogg Switchboard and Supply Company, Chicago. Edwards, with whom Kettering had had contact in his telephone work and in his work at NCR on the O.K. Charge Phone, had in fact given some help to them in developing the new system. By agreeing now to undertake the making of the 8,000 ignition sets in his factory, Edwards solved the manufacturing problem for the little company.

It was then that Kettering resigned from NCR to devote his full time to the ignition work. But Deeds continued on at NCR as general manager.

Kettering surely needed all his time now to work on ignition; for, as it turned out, there was much more to selling the new system to Cadillac than getting Leland to agree to put it on the car. Kettering still had a real fight to convince all the others at Cadillac of the merits of the new system. But this man, whom Leland called "an absolutely unknown young electrical genius," succeeded in selling not only his product but also himself to everyone at Cadillac with whom he had to deal.

Leland was a most exacting and critical purchaser. He found fault with many things about the new system. Trying to satisfy him and everyone else concerned, and to solve the unexpected problems that arose, Kettering began a long period of traveling the triangle Dayton, Detroit, Chicago, and of working even harder and longer than he had before. His address then, he said, was lower 4, car 236. In that time he learned to relax and sleep so well on night trains that he was able to spend night after night in sleeping cars without reducing his capacity for work in the daytime.

It was in this period that he began making automobile trips to Detroit also, and he made many of them. Once during those early months when Kettering was working so intensively, Mrs. Kettering called Dr. H. H. Herman, their family doctor and friend, and asked him to go over to the barn and see Charlie. "He's sick," she said.

Dr. Herman found that Kettering had a temperature of 102. "You must come with me and go home in my car," Dr. Herman told him. "You should go to bed, or you may get pneumonia."

No, he couldn't do that, Kettering told Dr. Herman. He was scheduled to be in Detroit the next day and was going to drive a test car up that night. Over the unpaved and unmarked roads of that time, such a drive of more than 200 miles was a formidable undertaking. Disregarding Dr. Herman's advice, Kettering did undertake it.

Furthermore, when he got back to Dayton later, he called Dr. Herman and said in his roguish way: "Doc, have you

65

got anybody else who is threatened with pneumonia? If you have, tell him to get in an open car and take a long drive with the snow blowing in his face. That's what I did, and I'm all right again."

It was during this critical period that two mysterious and unexpected difficulties arose.

The first trouble was that just after starting the engine there would sometimes be a short period of occasional misfiring when the engine would hesitate and might even stop altogether. The trouble was so mysterious and elusive that at first Kettering was completely baffled. But after many daytime and nighttime hours of observation he noticed that there could be a condition when, instead of a good spark, there would be only a weak corona, too ineffectual to fire the charge. Then he found that that happened only when the negative terminal of the coil was connected to the spark plug and that the trouble could be cured completely merely by making the high-tension terminal of the coil positive. Before that, no one knew that it made any difference which wire went to the spark plug.

But no sooner had he found how to cure that mysterious trouble in cold motors and the Kellogg people had begun to deliver ignition sets to Cadillac than there came another distress call from Detroit. There was sticking in the holding coil, or ignition relay, which was the heart of the new system. The trouble was so serious that the system just didn't work. Up at the Cadillac factory in Detroit, Kettering experimented all day in search of the difficulty, but altogether without success. What could be the difference between those factory-made relays and the experimental ones on which all the running had been done so successfully before?

"I chucked the Kellogg relays into my grip and got the midnight train to Dayton," Kettering recalled. "I remember I had an upper berth and had my grip up there with me.

I was mighty worried and couldn't sleep. I reached into my grip and got one of those relays out in the dark. I began feeling the pole pieces and the armature."

In that way he found that the end of the core, instead of being perfectly flat, was a little rounded. It could be felt better in the dark than seen in the light. That rounding, he knew, would concentrate the magnetism, thereby holding the armature tighter against the pole piece than was intended and thus not setting it free when needed.

"Then I went to sleep," Kettering recalled. "The train got into Dayton at five. I got right up and hurried over to the barn. I machined those pole pieces down flat. There wasn't a bit more trouble. I got back on the next train and took them to Detroit."

There was still another difficulty that had to be met and solved meanwhile—the patent problem. A search had shown that there were two existing patents with which the new system seemed to conflict to some degree. But fortunately Deeds was able to make satisfactory agreements with the holders of those patents, neither of which was being applied in practice at all.

After that first struggle was over, Leland told Kettering and Deeds, "I really felt sorry for you fellows. But every time you did something more the system got better. Finally, though, I really did not have the heart to find fault any more."

But then, and throughout his career, it was a hard and fast rule of Kettering's personally to see that whatever product he had to do with was made right. This was one of the chief reasons for the success he had in developing new products.

IX

IN THE SUMMER OF 1910 a woman, driving an automobile across the old Belle Isle bridge in Detroit, stalled her engine. That was a mishap not at all unusual at the time. But it was noteworthy for the reason that it contributed in a major way to bringing on the automobile self-starter.

A man who happened by just then stopped and offered to crank the woman's engine for her. He was Byron T. Carter, maker of the automobile called the Cartercar. Unfortunately, the spark was not retarded. So the engine kicked back and the flying crank broke Carter's jaw. Broken bones and other injuries were common when cars were cranked by hand. But Carter was not a young man, and complications arising out of the accident caused his death.

Now, it happened that Carter was a friend of Henry Leland, head man at Cadillac. Soon afterward, in Leland's office, Kettering remarked that he thought it would be possible to do away with the hand crank, sometimes called the "arm-strong starter," by cranking cars electrically. In Leland's distress at the loss of his friend Carter, he took up the suggestion at once. If Kettering could develop a successful self-starter, he would agree to put it on the Cadillac car the next year.

Kettering assured Leland that that would be possible, and he was ready to dive into the project with all his might. Just as with the cash register, the apparatus needed to crank an automobile engine, he knew, was not an electric motor big enough to turn it continuously. All he had to have was a small motor capable of putting forth a momentary but sufficiently vigorous burst of turning power.

From Leland's office Kettering hurried to his laboratory in the Deeds barn at Dayton. By furious work, a makeshift electric starting device was assembled out of available parts and so got ready for a test in record time. Then they threw in the switch and, hurrah! it cranked the engine in impressive fashion.

That was only the beginning of the extensive program of development, of course, but it demonstrated the fallacy of the common belief of the time that it was not possible to crank an automobile engine with an electric motor because the motor would have to be too big to go on a car. Some said that to start an automobile engine would take a 5-horsepower electric motor, one nearly as big as the engine itself. Scoffing at that idea, Leland said he never knew he was that strong and he had been cranking engines right along. Before that time, people had tried various ways of starting automobile engines, using springs, compressed air, and other means, but none of the schemes was really successful.

Now Kettering and his assistants began the task of working out an electric self-starter that would operate from a small storage battery and could be fitted to the Cadillac engine. Kettering's plan was to have an electric power unit that would be a satisfactory motor for cranking the engine as well as a generator for feeding electricity back into the battery and keeping it charged. So he devised a 6-24 volt system which in the starting position operated at 24 volts but in the running position fed electricity back into the battery at 6 volts. To do that he had to build an elaborate switching mechanism similar to the streetcar controller of that time.

The group working in the Deeds barn, whole or part time, now grew to about a dozen men and came to be known as the "barn gang." Some of these men had worked at NCR with Kettering. Among them, besides Bill Chryst, the balance wheel of the outfit, were the dynamic Bill Anderson; the talented draftsman, Bob DeMaree, and his capable young assistant, Zerbe C. Bradford; the all-round electricians, Bill Mooney and John Sheats; and the able mechanics, W. G. Johns, John Lipes, Harvey Phillips, and Walter Schiewetz.

The "barn gang" came to refer to Kettering as Boss Ket, and that name has stuck to him throughout his life. But the only difference in rank among the men who worked in the barn, Kettering said, "was when one guy was ranker than another."

As for the working hours kept by the men in the barn, one of them put it this way: "Say! Quit at five o'clock? Boy, we didn't know there was any five o'clock. All we knew was light and dark." To help relieve the tedium of the long hours, DeMaree brought in an old phonograph. There was only one record, *When You and I Were Young, Maggie,* but it was played over and over and over again.

The first of the experimental starters to be fitted to a Cadillac engine was given its initial trial on Christmas Eve, 1910. As Kettering recalled the events then, "This machine proved to have the torque necessary but was slightly larger than was practical to put on the engine. We immediately started redesigning, got the patterns made and some of the castings out, when it was found that it was advisable to reduce it still further. We then made the second step in the design. This machine was finished up, installed on a Cadillac car, and delivered to the Cadillac Motor Car Company on February 17, 1911. This car performed very satisfactorily and went through all the Cadillac tests."

That was Kettering's simple account of the progress in the final months of the development. But it makes no mention of the trials and tribulations that accompanied those events. Out of his years of experience Kettering said once:

"Developmental work is always a slightly organized chaos."

The difficulties arose partly out of the high pressure under which the work had to be done. Leland was going off soon on his winter vacation, and he had to approve the new starter personally.

It was during this period that the late Thomas J. Watson, then sales manager of NCR and later head of the International Business Machines Corporation, had the experience of being—as he thought—the first man, outside of the little group directly concerned with the electric self-starter, to have it demonstrated to him. One day as Watson got off the train in Dayton he met Kettering and Henry Leland. Leland was taking the train back to Detroit after a visit to Dayton. Seeing Watson, Kettering said to him, "Wait for me in the station, Tom, and I'll drive you home."

When Kettering came back they went to his car and both got in. Watson recalled that he chuckled to himself at that, thinking that here this absent-minded inventor was just getting into his car and forgetting to crank the engine. But, to his astonishment, Kettering merely set some controls, pushed a button, and the engine started.

In his amazement, Watson asked what in the world that gadget was. At that Kettering invited him to get out and he showed him just what he had there under the hood. That demonstration and ride to his home afterward made Watson the first member of the public to have that historic experience.

On February 10 word came that Leland would leave for his vacation in Bermuda on the seventeenth, just a week later. Then, in the effort to finish up the operating model and get it off to Detroit in time for Leland to approve, began the most strenuous week of the whole endeavor. The men toiled until they became so dull-headed that mistakes were made—mistakes which interfered with progress. But at last the tired gang heard with the greatest gratification and relief the cheerful sound for which their long efforts had been expended, the engine being briskly cranked and starting with a roar.

One of those who rode in that car as it was driven to the station that night to be sent off to Detroit by express, L. B. Case, a friend of Bob DeMaree's, remembers that Kettering stopped the engine and started it again in almost every block—as if to reassure himself that it was going to work when Leland and his men tried it out the next day. And not once did it fail to start.

The next day in Detroit, with Kettering on hand, Leland tried out the new self-starter and liked it. So Delco was given an order for 12,000 units to go on all 1912 model Cadillac cars.

This was a most gratifying outcome. But it brought on further difficulties, of course. One of these was finding a source of supply of a storage battery suitable for use with the self-starter. Battery makers did not believe that it was practical to crank an automobile with a small storage battery.

One day a letter signed C. F. Kettering had come to the Electric Storage Battery Company. It asked for a quotation on 10,000 storage batteries. Nobody in all history had ordered 10,000 batteries at one time. And, as for the Dayton Engineering Laboratories Company, the battery company had never heard of it.

But O. Lee Harrison, one of the company's salesmen, was sent to Dayton to see Kettering. "I don't want to sell you any batteries" was the way Harrison greeted him. "I just want to look at a fellow who thinks he wants to buy that many batteries."

However, Harrison was impressed with Kettering and with what he said and demonstrated about the self-starter. Not for nothing had Kettering spent his time with the sales people at NCR and taken that night course in salesmanship. However, Harrison found it difficult to get his people to make a battery small enough to go on a car. But at last he succeeded in getting one to meet the size limitations, and one that was rugged enough, as well, to stand the jolting of a moving automobile. Later, at the invitation of Deeds, Harrison joined the staff of Delco as sales manager.

Now that there was to be a storage battery and an electric generator on the Cadillac car it was decided to do away with the acetylene lights and to put on electric lights—thus eliminating the storage cylinder on the running board and the nuisance of having to get out and strike matches to light the headlights. The electrical system to be furnished by Delco in accordance with that new arrangement thus consisted of three units: the self-starter, the battery systems of ignition (there were two, as the original dry-cell system was retained also), and electric lights. Of these only the starting and ignition units had been developed as yet, and those but partially.

It was the situation with battery ignition all over again. "We still had all kinds of skepticism to meet and overcome," Kettering recalled. But it was because he was continually on the ground in person, working directly with the men at Cadillac who had to test and pass on new things, that his efforts were successful. He did not spend his time in the front office. He went right out and worked with the men on the job, and whenever any bug developed he saw to it that it was located and corrected.

He had an absolute disregard for his own time and convenience—and for his appearance as well. "You should have seen him get down into the guts of an automobile and fish out the trouble," said Herman Schwarze, master electrician at Cadillac and a man who became Kettering's loyal friend. "He would come in all dressed up and go away looking like a greasy bum. He never could take too much trouble helping us when we were in a jam."

One day in the early spring—it was April 12, 1911—Kettering was driving his test car over a slippery road near Dayton when it took him off the highway into a ditch. In that accident he got a foot caught between the pedals and came out of it with a broken ankle.

What with the high pressure under which the work had to be done because the new model deadline was so near, that accident looked like disaster enough. But hardly had it happened when down from Detroit came still more disheartening news. There had been a fire in the garage, and the precious car equipped with the only other complete self-starter and new electrical system had been badly damaged.

That car simply had to be put into operation again, and no one else had been able to do it. So, after only two days in bed with his broken ankle, Kettering sent for crutches and took the night train to Detroit. There, with the help of Herman Schwarze, he got the trouble remedied.

Under pressure of the circumstances, he continued then to hobble around on his crutches and to go about his business in spite of his broken ankle. Bill Chryst recalled that one night when he got on the Detroit sleeper in the Dayton station the Pullman porter said to him, "That man with the broken leg is on here again."

Meanwhile, remembering the experience with battery ignition, Deeds had had a search made for possible patent interference. In doing so, the men ran smack into a patent taken out by Clyde J. Coleman. The Coleman patent was merely a paper patent in that it had not been put to use at all; but it did specify the essential features of the electric self-starter.

Deeds set off at once for New York to see Conrad Hubert, owner of the Coleman patent; and that night on the train was for him the longest he had ever put in, he said. But, fortunately, he found Hubert willing to give him a license under the Coleman patent at satisfactory terms. Hubert was quite willing to do that, in fact, for he did not consider an electric self-starter of much practical importance.

Then there was again the big problem of how the starter and the other equipment to fill that order from Cadillac were to be made. As heads of the Dayton Engineering Laboratories Company, Kettering and Deeds still wanted to keep it a development concern and not let it become a manufacturing company. Every effort was accordingly made to find manufacturers who would contract to make the equipment. But, although Kellogg continued to make the battery ignition, and although some other companies agreed to supply other parts, it became necessary for Delco itself to step up to the job of manufacturing a large part of the equipment.

They rented space, therefore, and set up to perform the manufacturing and assembly operations required. At first the space rented was a mere 40 by 80 feet on one floor of a Dayton building and there were only twelve men on the payroll. But to get even that small endeavor under way Kettering and Deeds had to put in all the money they could scrape up, and they mortgaged everything they had besides. Deeds put a mortgage on his house and Kettering on a lot that he owned. Both borrowed money on their life insurance policies. They also put up their patents and the contract with Cadillac as collateral for a loan from the bank, and Cadillac paid them some money in advance. They sold some preferred stock, too, and raised money in every way possible.

A debt of gratitude was due Henry Leland for not losing heart through it all, said Deeds. Leland had, in fact, been advised by persons of prominence and influence in the electrical field not to put an electric self-starter on the Cadillac car. It will ruin you, they warned. So firmly did Leland believe in the self-starter, however, that he proposed leaving the hand crank off the new model when it came out and depending altogether on the self-starter, as is commonly done now. "Oh, no," his associates protested, "you can't do that."

"Why not?" Leland asked. "Haven't you any faith in your starter?"

Sure, they had faith in it, but not quite that much. Then it came out that Leland had already had the hand crank taken off the experimental car. He had had it hidden in his garage for a month, and the men working with the car and using the self-starter every day had not missed it.

After the 1912 model Cadillac had come out, Kettering was invited to speak on the self-starter at a meeting of the American Institute of Electrical Engineers. He had one of the starters there for display and demonstration and he told the gathering of electrical men just what he had done, why he had made the motor and the battery so small and why he had made wires carry currents for short periods five times the amount set by the electrical engineer as the maximum allowable for continuous use.

After his presentation, Kettering recalled, "One of those dignified gentlemen that ought to have been wearing striped pants and tails gets up and says: 'No wonder this man can make a self-starter. He transgresses every fundamental law of electrical engineering. If you want to make a self-starter that way you are welcome to it. I'm an honorable electrical engineer, and I refuse to do that.'" But, as Kettering remarked, "All human development, no matter what form it takes, must be outside the rules; otherwise, we would never have anything new."

"For the work it had to do, the self-starter did look funny to the central station designer," Kettering agreed. But those electrical engineers did not understand that "a self-starter must be 90 per cent automobile and 10 per cent electrical apparatus."

"Never mind about the experts" was a remark Kettering often made. The public liked the self-starter. "They never troubled their heads about whether the theory was right or not," he said. "Inside of two years it was pretty hard to find anyone who wasn't thoroughly sold on the idea. Cars that were not equipped with the new device . . . simply faded right out of the picture."

X

"NOBODY," KETTERING HAS SAID, "is smart enough to go into the business he ends up in." That saying comes in part out of his experience in the Dayton Engineering Laboratories Company, which had been forced to depart from its original objective of developing new ideas to become a manufacturing concern. Now, in the second year of Delco starting and ignition, its use was extended to seven cars: Cadillac, Hudson, Packard, Cole, Oldsmobile, Oakland, and Jackson. Meanwhile, to supply the fast-rising demand, factory space had had to be expanded rapidly from the original 40 by 80 feet on one floor to a five-story building covering half a city block, while the number of workers increased from 12 to 1,200.

That extension of the use of Delco equipment to so many cars all within a few months, and to many more later, naturally brought on a host of pressing engineering problems. Fortunately, in the previous fall the force for tackling such problems had received a valuable addition. W. A. Chryst, Kettering's able assistant at NCR, and in the pioneering work in the Deeds barn as well, joined the staff at Delco as chief engineer. During that first year also an important improvement in the Delco self-starter had been made by simplifying it through doing away with the 24-volt part of the circuit and the complicated switching mechanism that was a part of it.

During all those early years of expansion and changing models there was a constant drive on to meet some new demand. A great deal of night work had to be done and Kettering was in the thick of it. During that period he was constantly harried by troubles and hurried in his conscientious efforts to satisfy the users of Delco products.

Returning from an absence, he would throw his grip in the corner of his office. So demanding were problems and tasks that he was likely to leave again without so much as an opportunity to go home and get a change of linen. One morning while on a trip he stood in the washroom of a sleeping car with his collar in his hand and remarked to Louis Ruthenburg, a member of the Delco staff who was with him, that he couldn't decide which side of that collar to wear outside. He had already worn it on both sides, and he didn't know which looked worse.

Because he was away from home so much of the time, traveling here and there about his business, Mrs. Kettering was naturally left alone a great deal. She was not given to complaining or nagging, but sometimes when he was absent on one of his frequent trips she would take their son Gene and go to visit her parents in Ashland.

Kettering had to make so many trips that he sometimes had trouble keeping up with himself, in fact. Once when he went to take the train he found that he did not have his ticket. The conductor said, "Just go ahead, Mr. Kettering. We'll fix you up."

"It isn't that," he replied. "Without that ticket, I don't know just where I'm supposed to go."

Not all his traveling was done on the railroad, by any means. He also frequently drove to Detroit and elsewhere by automobile. There were few paved roads then and next to no road markings. Richard Harfst, then at Cadillac but later manager of the Automobile Club of Michigan, recalled a time when he and Kettering drove all night from Dayton to Detroit. Driving hour after hour through the rain and mud was for Harfst a disagreeable experience; but Kettering delighted in it.

Although Kettering was an exceptionally good driver, he had what is called a heavy foot. Once when he was driving a Cadillac test car outside Detroit, Bill Blaine, the Cadillac test driver beside him, said, with admirable diplomacy, "Boss, maybe you had better change speed here."

"Why so?" said Kettering, not wanting to slow his test just then.

"Well, there's a bridge out up ahead. You're going a little too fast to turn out but not quite fast enough to jump it."

Not all the problems Kettering had to deal with then related to the self-starter. Part of them were concerned with battery ignition. For one thing, the magneto people were using their best ingenuity to convince automobile users that battery ignition was not so good as magneto. A big Cadillac dealer in Pittsburgh kept insisting to the Cadillac people that for the Cadillac car a magneto would be better than the Delco battery ignition they were using. He could demonstrate it, he said.

The prominence of the dealer made this case seem so important that Henry Leland and Kettering went to Pittsburgh together to look into his claim. There a man from the magneto company, who had installed a magneto on the Cadillac car along with the battery ignition, demonstrated that driving up a certain hill on battery ignition the car would stall before it reached the top; but that, in a repeat run with magneto ignition, it would go clear to the top. He demonstrated that again and again.

When lunchtime came, Kettering remarked that he did not care for lunch that day; he would just stay there and check over the battery ignition a little, and maybe they could then make another test after lunch. When the men returned, the magneto man showed again that with the switch on "battery" the car stalled part way up the hill, just as before lunch; but with the switch on "magneto" it went right up the hill without hesitation.

Leland was shocked by that demonstration, so apparently convincing of the superiority of the magneto. "Why didn't you find this out, Ket, and tell me?" asked the worried president, as he stroked his white beard nervously.

"Well," was the reply, "from the demonstrations here to-day, it does look bad, Mr. Leland. I'll grant you that. But I should tell you that while you men were at lunch I interchanged the wires at the switch. This afternoon when you thought the car stalled because it was running on the battery it was actually running on the magneto, and the other way around."

The demonstrator had merely taken advantage of a peculiarity of the Cadillac carburetor of that time. It performed best when the throttle was opened gradually, not when it was snapped open quickly. Kettering knew that and had used his ingenuity to outwit the magneto man at his own game.

Putting electric lights on cars naturally reduced the use of acetylene, which before had been the standard means of lighting automobiles. The principal supplier of acetylene was the Prest-O-Lite Company, the head of which was Carl Fisher, who later became an important developer of property in Florida. Out of their associations, Fisher and Kettering became fast friends. And twenty years later Fisher gave a dinner in Florida in honor of his good friend Ket. On that occasion Fisher said, "This is the only dinner any man ever gave to the fellow who put him out of business." Actually, the use of acetylene in oxyacetylene welding, which expanded as the number of automobiles increased, made not quite true what Fisher said about having been put out of business.

One immediate effect of eliminating the armstrong

method of starting engines was a big increase in the number of women driving automobiles. Speaking once to a gathering of young women, Malcolm Bingay, long editor of the Detroit *Free Press,* said that by developing the self-starter Kettering "did more to emancipate women than Susan B. Anthony or Mrs. Pankhurst or all the other valiant gals who get the credit he deserves."

For this reason, the self-starter was a potent factor in expanding the use of the automobile and making it more useful. In the five years following the introduction of the electric self-starter in 1911, the number of automobiles manufactured and sold increased by more than sevenfold. That big five-year gain, in fact, marked the beginning of an upward trend in number of automobiles in use, a trend both fast and long-sustained.

There was a demand for the self-starter on the other side of the Atlantic, too. Over there the demand was intensified by an unfortunate accident involving the children of the famous dancer, Isadora Duncan. Isadora Duncan's children were in an automobile in Paris which, when hand-cranked by the chauffeur, started off without a driver and ran into the Seine, drowning the children.

About that time the European rights for Delco electrical equipment were sold to a concern in Germany. To help get the European agents started off right, J. H. Hunt of the Delco experimental staff, accompanied by Lawrence Langner, who had been handling foreign patents for Delco, made a trip to Germany. This is the same Lawrence Langner who later founded the Theater Guild.

Although Delco had been the first to introduce the electric self-starter, it did not long remain the only supplier. In March, 1913, less than two years after the self-starter appeared on Cadillac, forty-four makes of electrical starting, lighting, and ignition equipment were listed in the trade journal *Horseless Age*. Delco continued to be the leader in the field, however. This dominance was due in part to the superior technical efforts of Kettering and his associates and in part to the Delco policy that if a mistake was made it was corrected, whatever the cost.

Because of Kettering's belief in the importance of change, the experimental and engineering facilities at Delco were far in advance of those maintained by most other industrial concerns of that time. The little laboratory in the Deeds barn had since grown into one occupying the whole top floor of the Delco plant. That space was given over to an experimental and research department, an engineering group, and a model shop. In that laboratory was one of the first electrical dynamometers in the automobile industry for measuring the horsepower output and behavior of engines and accessory equipment. The laboratory came to have much other apparatus also, including a second and third dynamometer and a cold room where the starting of cars could be tested at low temperatures.

In the spring of 1913 disaster struck the factory of the new Delco Company in the form of the great Dayton flood. Water rose in the Delco Plant to a height of twenty-seven feet. The interruption came at a most critical time when every effort was needed to meet the heavy spring demand of automobile makers using Delco equipment.

Kettering was in Chicago when news of the disaster reached him. He started to Dayton by the first train. But, because of the extensiveness of the flood, the train could take him only as far as Richmond, Indiana, more than forty miles west of Dayton. He and Bill Anderson, who was with him, hired a car and set out to drive from there. At Lewisburg, Ohio, they found washed away the highway bridge over the large stream east of the town. But the bridge of the electric railway was still standing. So they daringly bumped across the flood on the bare ties of that bridge, and thus at last made it to Dayton.

Kettering knew that at the Delco plant the automatic machines on the first floor were underwater and the basement, where was stored almost the entire stock, was full of water and slime. He called the Ahrens-Fox Fire Engine Company at Cincinnati, borrowed a fire engine from them, and with it pumped out the basement of the plant.

He and his men stayed there at the factory day and night, sleeping on the floor and living on what food they could get. By prodigious efforts they got the plant going again in time to avoid hindering seriously the manufacture of Delco-equipped automobiles.

In April, 1915, Deeds resigned his position at the National Cash Register Company and began to devote all his time and business talents to Delco. Prior to that time he had not been publicly designated as president of the new company. Nevertheless, he had been managing the business affairs of the concern by remote control.

In all the endeavors undertaken by Delco, the association of Kettering and Deeds was an admirable one. Deeds, as a first-rank administrator and business manager, was a perfect complement to Kettering who, as an originator and developer of new ideas and products, wanted to keep clear of business affairs as much as possible.

One day in 1916 Kettering was working away in the experimental department at Delco when Deeds came in and said to him, "Well, Ket, you know we've been discussing a deal with United Motors for some time. We are to get nine million dollars for Delco, part cash and part stock."

"That's a heck of a lot of money" was Kettering's only comment, as he went ahead with what he was working on.

The sale of Delco came about after Deeds and Kettering

Double desk of Kettering and Deeds at Delco in the early years of the company. Mostly, as here, the two men were too busy elsewhere to get in the picture.

Airplane with all-cantilever wing structure and other advances built just after World War I under Kettering's guidance and sponsorship. Standing on the wings to demonstrate strength were, from the left: Howard Rinehart, James Jacobs, J. P. Henry, Harvey Geyer, B. L. Whelan, Wallace Whittaker, Thomas Midgley, Jr., J. H. Hunt, Milton K. Bauman (chief designer), Harold E. Talbott, G. M. Williams, and Kettering.

Wright Model-B airplane in which Kettering had his first flight about 1912. This photograph, taken by Kettering himself, shows pilot Howard Rinehart with W. A. Chryst in another flight on the same day.

had been approached by representatives of W. C. Durant, who was then organizing a syndicate of automobile accessory companies to be given the name of United Motors Corporation. For Delco, the negotiations were all handled by Deeds, Kettering having no active part in them.

In an announcement of the change to Delco employees, printed in *Delco Doings,* the company house organ, Deeds said: "The organization of Delco will in no wise be affected by the new association. . . . Mr. Kettering and I will continue to administer the affairs of the company."

One important effect of amalgamating Delco with United Motors Corporation was that it brought Kettering into association with Alfred P. Sloan, Jr., who had had an important part in organizing the new concern and who was made president of it. As a young engineer, Sloan had first demonstrated his capabilities by making a successful concern out of the nearly defunct Hyatt Roller Bearing Company. He was destined soon to be the principal architect of the present General Motors Corporation, of which he was to serve as president for fourteen years and as chairman of the board for nineteen. Thus the association of Kettering and Sloan, which began in that year of 1916, came to mean much to the two men, to the automobile industry, and indeed to the nation.

From Kettering's viewpoint, the period from 1911 to 1916 was the golden age of Delco. It was then that new things, pioneering things, were being done. And one of his principal characteristics is that the intensity of his interest in any new undertaking extends only to the time when he can get it going in good shape.

The way to tell whether a new development is over the hump, he once remarked, is to try taking your hands off it. If it runs back at you, it has not been pushed far enough. But, if it continues to go forward, then it is far enough along for the research man to leave it to others.

85

As throughout his life, Kettering had many other activities during the Delco years, even though his schedule of work appeared to leave little time for anything else. He began to give, both before Delco people and outside groups, the science lectures and other talks which he enjoyed so much; he and Chryst developed the system of engine, generator, and storage battery described in a later chapter to bring electric light and power to farms; and he helped to found an engineers' club in Dayton. As a headquarters for the Dayton Engineers' Club, Kettering and Deeds erected the beautiful and commodious building at Monument Avenue and Jefferson Street. They built it about 1917 at a cost of more than $300,000.

Professor Frank D. Slutz, head of Moraine Park School to be mentioned presently, has related an event at one of the annual parties of the Dayton Engineers' Club—an event which illustrated one of Kettering's distinctive characteristics. As a stunt to entertain those in attendance, the committee wired six of the chairs around the banquet table so that when a switch was thrown the men sitting on those chairs would get a whale of an electric shock. They saw to it that Kettering sat on one of those chairs.

At the proper time during the banquet, Professor Slutz arose and said that he would like to nominate for membership in the Dayton Engineers' Club a man who had suffered severe injustice from the American public because of his courageous opposition to World War I. "This man in now languishing in prison in Atlanta," he said. "His name is Eugene Debs. Will all those in favor of making Debs a member of this club please rise."

At that instant the switch in the line to the wired chairs was thrown and five prominent members of the club jumped to their feet with amazing alacrity. But not Kettering! Although his chair fairly sizzled with electricity, he sat still and took it.

What the men who pulled that stunt did not know perhaps was that Kettering had always handled electricity with indifference from the time when, as a telephone worker and experimenter, he had touched bare wires to his tongue to see if there was any current in them, to that when he was accustomed even to handling "hot" ignition wires with his bare hands. Bill Chryst recalled that, when experimenting with engines, Boss Ket would sometimes put four of his fingers on the spark plugs of a 4-cylinder engine as a convenient, if not pleasant, means of stopping it.

With some of the money Kettering received when Delco became a part of United Motors, he soon undertook an interesting experiment. It was an effort to assist in establishing a successful manufacturing business in a small town— in his home town of Loudonville, Ohio. He wanted to give a lift to the town and at the same time try to find out whether a small-town manufacturing enterprise of the sort he had in mind could be a real success.

Hugo H. Young had invented a motorcycle sidecar with which the motorcycle could be banked in rounding curves. Young had got a patent on his invention and in a little shop in Loudonville was making a few of the vehicles for sale. He called his organization the Flxible Side Car Company, having left out the "e" to get a trade-mark on the name.

Kettering went to see Hugo Young and offered to give his organization a boost by becoming an important investor in the little company. His offer was accepted, and the experiment he began then proved ultimately to be successful—but not, as will appear later, until after it had passed through some hardships.

Because Kettering lived in Dayton and knew the Wright Brothers, he early became interested in flying. His first airplane flight was made at the flying school operated by Orville Wright, with Howard M. Rinehart as pilot. The place was near Dayton on the site of what is now Patterson Field, and the time about 1912. As Kettering recalls it, the airplane in which he was given his first flight was "one of the very old Wright models where you sit out in front with a couple of sticks in front of you."

Kettering admired Wilbur and Orville Wright and all they did in overcoming obstacles to successful flight. Those obstacles were psychological as well as physical, for it was commonly believed then that heavier-than-air flight was impossible. "The Wright Brothers," Kettering said, "flew right through the smoke screen of impossibility."

He soon became enthusiastic about flying. With Rinehart as pilot, he flew a great deal. At that early time when the airplane was in its infancy, said Rinehart, few other men of Kettering's prominence were flying. People thus talked about his flying exploits, and what he did and said had a large influence in furthering interest and advancing activity in aviation. "This thing is coming," Kettering would say. "There isn't anything to stop it. . . . We must accept it with an open mind." He overlooked obstacles, of which there were many at that time, and went ahead anyway, Rinehart said. Whenever in their airplane flights any work on the plane had to be done, Kettering was out and in the thick of it.

As with everything else Kettering did, his flying was reflected in his philosophy. "Everyone ought to take a ride in an airplane," he said early. "If an airplane passenger has any personal conceit, such an experience will remove it before he again reaches the ground. If the general manager of some great factory reaches an altitude of 5,000 feet, looks back and sees a little bit of a factory about the size of a postage stamp, he is bound to realize that he is not so much after all. . . . I said, the first time I went up, that it looked to me very foolish to quarrel about two feet on a line fence, one side or the other."

During the Delco years Kettering had a part also in organizing and guiding the Moraine Park School. This was a private school in Dayton for grades one to twelve, an experiment in secondary education. The suggestion for the school came originally from Arthur E. Morgan, then head of the Miami Conservancy District, an organization for constructing dams to prevent a repetition of the disastrous Dayton flood of 1913.

The plan was to establish a school of limited size to prepare boys and girls for leadership in life by emphasizing "initiative, and courage, and variety, and ingenuity." Dr. Frank D. Slutz, who had been a successful high school principal and superintendent of schools in Colorado, was chosen director of the new school.

The first problem was that of providing a building for the school. To solve it temporarily, Kettering offered the use of his greenhouse. This was the place where, out of his intense interest in how things grow, he had been experimenting with growing plants under special conditions. Among other projects carried on there, he had been growing cucumbers of enormous size. Saying that he "would rather raise kids than cucumbers," Kettering made that greenhouse available as a temporary home for the new school. Two of the students who entered the junior division of the Moraine Park School were Gene Kettering and the girl who later became his wife, Virginia Weiffenbach. Both continued on there through high school.

In general, the experiment of the Moraine Park School, which extended for ten years, was successful, Kettering thought. But he was old-fashioned enough to believe that, among all the interesting and progressive activities the students had there, not enough time and drill were devoted to such common but essential subjects as reading, spelling, and arithmetic. He thought, too, that students should have been assigned sufficiently difficult tasks and have had enough interest in their studies to do some homework.

In spite of being so deeply engrossed in his many endeavors, Kettering found time to spend with Gene—more time than you would think, said Dr. Slutz. He had a way of dropping in on Gene at school or other places. Gene was a member of the Boy Scouts. And when he and his fellows went out to the woods Kettering would sometimes go with them. In every way he could he tried to teach Gene. He led him along by arousing his interest in everyday things and by showing him that he could have fun with them.

Once he and Gene kept some crawfish in one of the bathtubs in their home. They piled stones in the tub to make a home for the crawfish. This was part of Kettering's efforts to arouse Gene's interest in nature and to teach him some of the habits of nature's creatures. As a boy, Kettering had watched the crawfish in Big Run Creek near his farm home. In later life he made use of the crawfish's habit of scuttling backwards to illustrate his thinking, when he said that, in view of the way we nearly always seem to go at things backwards, human nature must have been ancestored by the crawfish.

He and Mrs. Kettering began early a successful effort to teach Gene the value of money. The allowance of spending money he had as a boy was kept small and he was taught to make an accounting of the money spent while he was at summer camp. Nevertheless, as Kettering once said to the Reverend L. O. Bricker, "I have never been a heavy father. I have never said to my son, 'You must do this or that, or you've got to do thus and so, because I tell you.'" Instead, he had a habit of teaching Gene mostly by suggestion and example.

It was during the early Delco years that the Ketterings built their beautiful home, Ridgeleigh Terrace. Situated in the countryside near Dayton, it looks out from a hilltop over the broad Miami Valley. A pipe organ for Mrs. Kettering was built into the home. Partly for the protection of that organ and partly because Kettering thought that houses in that climate ought to have it anyway, he installed also a complete system of air conditioning.

So far as Kettering knows, his was the first air-conditioned home in America. At any rate, the air-conditioning equipment was put in against the advice of the architect and the contractor. "They threw up their hands at my suggestion," Kettering recalled. "So I bought what was needed to harness a well-understood scientific principle and made my own air-conditioning plant. That is just one of the compensations of being an independent sort of mechanic."

The back-and-forth banter in the conversation over the telephone that day when Charlie Kettering first talked to Olive Williams in Ashland, and the playful spirit he had, were never lost throughout their years together. One day Mrs. Kettering was to give a luncheon for a group of her women friends at Ridgeleigh Terrace. Kettering happened to drop in briefly while preparations were under way. Seeing the table in the dining room immaculately arranged, he called the help and directed them to take everything off and to put at each place a saucer of milk. Then he disappeared—chuckling as he went.

The Ketterings moved to Ridgeleigh Terrace in 1914. Some of their best years were spent there—years when their son Gene was growing from boyhood to young manhood. They entertained many people there, distinguished visitors, business associates of Kettering, women friends of Mrs. Kettering, and many others. But, unfortunately, as will appear later, the years they lived there were not really many.

XI

As an electrical engineer, Kettering thought he ought to be able to give his mother on the farm near Loudonville the luxury of electric lights and electric power. He wanted to set her free of the kerosine [1] lamp with its dim light and its need to be tended each day, of the outside well with its hand-operated pump, of the hand-power churn, and of other age-old contrivances which took so much of her time and strength.

It was then about 1913, well before the time when electric lines from central power stations had been run out into the country. So Kettering bought a little gasoline engine, a one-cylinder putt-putt, belted it to a small electric generator, and provided a set of storage batteries to be charged by the generator and thus to furnish a continuous electromotive force of 32 volts when the engine and generator were not running. He wired the farmhouse himself, and for the first time turned on electric lights at the old homestead. By contrast with what the elder Ketterings had been accustomed to all their lives, the result represented a marvelous improvement.

That outfit was not automatic, however. When the engine quit running, as it soon did for some reason, thus letting the batteries run down, the folks just went back to kerosine lamps. That experience made Kettering decide that he ought to face the problem and do a thorough job of developing a farm lighting outfit that would be dependable and foolproof.

[1] Those concerned with kerosine industrially and technically spell it with an "i" instead of an "e"—this to be consistent with gasoline and benzine, other products from the same source. Only the dictionary has not caught up.

Thus it was that, on top of all the intensive work then being done at Delco on starting, lighting, and ignition for automobiles, he set out to develop a dependable means of furnishing electricity to farms and country homes. After much work, he and his men came up with a small, one-cylinder, air-cooled engine directly driving an electric generator feeding into a set of sixteen lead-plate storage batteries in glass jars. The system was automatic in that turning on a light started the engine, which then stopped of itself when the batteries were full.

For making and selling the farm lighting plant thus developed, a new company was formed. It was first named the Domestic Engineering Company. But the farm lighting plant was named "Delco-Light." And some time afterward the company came to be called the Delco-Light Company. Deeds became president of the new concern and Kettering vice-president. Kettering took responsibility for the engineering success of the Delco-Light plant, and he made Lester S. Keilholtz, who had been chief designer at Delco, chief engineer and Ernest Dickey assistant chief engineer.

In R. H. Grant, the man put in charge of selling the new product, the company was especially fortunate. Grant, top-rank salesman at NCR for several years and a man whom Kettering and Deeds knew well, had himself suggested that he be given the job of selling the Delco-Light plant. Grant entered into that assignment with his customary enthusiasm.

The demand for the product and the effectiveness of Grant's sales organization proved to be so great that in that first year, 1916, the new company did a business of about two and a half million dollars. In part this was due also to the circumstance that Kettering had directed that the sale price of the outfits be set somewhat below cost, as computed for the early production. The company would rely on increasing volume to make the venture a profitable one, he

93

said. The sale price of the complete Delco-Light plant at the factory was thus set at $275.

The first advertisement of the Delco-Light plant in the *Saturday Evening Post*, "Electricity for Every Farm," run in September, 1916, said of the outfit in part: "It has a capacity of 40 to 50 lights, and is so simple that anyone can operate it. The turning of a switch starts it and it stops automatically when the batteries are full."

As with all new products in the hands of people, unforeseen difficulties and problems soon developed. Rapidly mounting sales made those problems all the more pressing. In his conscientious zeal to make the new product right, Kettering devoted much of his time and effort to correcting difficulties as they arose. Because of the pressure of other interests, he was likely to devote his evenings to experimenting on Delco-Light problems.

One of the troubles that developed came after the plants had been on the market only a short while. Suddenly pistons began sticking in running engines. The difficulty was so serious that Kettering spent many hours at the plant without a break—Mrs. Kettering even bringing him his meals—while he tried to locate the cause of the trouble. So far as could be seen, the pistons were all right, with proper clearances and in every other respect.

After having worked a long time without finding any clue to the source of the trouble, Kettering became so tired and exasperated that, to ease his feelings, he hurled one of the pistons at a concrete pillar. The piston smashed—and in doing so it showed him what was wrong. Because of a change in foundry practice, the thickness of the piston head was found to be only one-sixteenth of an inch, whereas it should have been three-sixteenths. The thin section did not carry away the heat of combustion fast enough. Thus the piston head expanded unduly, causing the piston to stick tight in the cylinder.

The biggest problem of all the many that developed, however, was introduced when insurance underwriters insisted that the little engines should not be run on gasoline because the fire rules permitted no more than a gallon of gasoline to be kept around a private home. Then we will just run them on kerosine, Kettering said. After all, the farmer has always been used to having kerosine around the house.

But then it was found that when run on kerosine the engines knocked badly. That knock was the same metallic sound sometimes heard in automobile engines when accelerating or pulling a hill. In that little air-cooled engine, however, the disturbance was very violent indeed. To get rid of that noisy and destructive knock the compression of the engine had to be reduced, and that lowered its output of power. But, as is related further on, the onset of that difficulty and the sacrifice that had to be made to cure it helped lead Kettering later to one of his most important developments, more knock-free gasoline.

Those little farm lighting sets came to be known and used far and wide. Edgar A. Guest, the poet and columnist, remembers a trip to Yucatán which he and a group of others made with Kettering some years ago to visit the Mayan ruins at Chichén Itzá. There was a little hacienda at that place with three or four rooms for visitors. When the party arrived, the woman in charge of the place was in distress. The Delco-Light plant which furnished light and electricity for the hacienda had stopped and refused to run. When Kettering learned about that, he asked to see the plant. He had it repaired and running in a few minutes. What an astonishing thing it was, said Edgar Guest, that the inventor of that little outfit should turn up there in the jungle and do a service job on it!

Delco-Light proved to be such a big boon to people living on farms and other places remote from sources of electric power that as many as 40,000 sets were purchased in a single year. But that was the peak of the business; for in a few years, with the extension through the country of high lines from central power stations, the demand for Delco-Light plants decreased rapidly. By educating country people to the advantages of electricity, Delco-Light was itself a factor in hastening that extension and so in bringing about its own displacement. As Bill Chryst expressed it, "The Delco-Light plant simply worked itself out of a job." As for the Delco-Light Company, it had been turning meanwhile to making the domestic refrigerator, Frigidaire, to the improvement of which Kettering had made large contributions.

To Kettering, one of the greatest gratifications he got out of the Delco-Light endeavor was that through it he had been able to provide modern conveniences for his father and mother on the farm during their lifetime. They not only had electric lights but also a modern water system, an electric refrigerator, an electric washer, an electric sweeper, and other conveniences.

Kettering wanted to go further and build a new home for his parents. But his mother said no, she was quite comfortable as she was. After a time, though, he did get her to consent to a modernization of the house, but with the stipulation that as much of the old house as possible be used in the new. Under that agreement, Kettering constructed a new and modern dwelling where the house of his boyhood had stood.

Kettering was deeply devoted to his mother. And while she lived he found time, in spite of the busy life he was leading, to make frequent trips from Dayton to Loudonville to visit her, mostly driving an automobile over the unpaved and sometimes distressingly muddy roads of that time.

Joe E. Butz, head of the Delco garage, made some of those trips to Loudonville with Kettering, and many other trips as well. Besides the bad roads, they had to contend also with the frequent tire trouble that went with automobile driving. When a tire did go flat, Kettering was always the first man out of the car, Butz said. He would grab the jack and push it under the car. By the time the tire was replaced, his clothes were likely to be plastered with mud. He took the same responsibility whenever he found a woman driver on the road with a flat tire. Sometimes on such occasions he was offered a tip by a grateful woman who had no idea who the tall stranger was.

During the early years of Delco and Delco-Light, the Honorable James M. Cox of Dayton, three times governor of Ohio, addressed a public gathering in Loudonville. Knowing that Kettering's home was at Loudonville, the governor spoke with admiration of the big things Kettering was doing for the people of Dayton through the new developments he had made and the prosperous companies which had come out of them.

After the address, many of those present came up to shake hands with the governor, as people do. The very last of them was a quiet country woman with a shawl over her shoulders. "I am Charlie Kettering's mother," she said to Governor Cox, "and I'm so proud and so grateful. I never thought that the governor would come to Loudonville and speak so about my boy."

XII

IN 1916 KETTERING made one of the important decisions of his lifetime. In his disappointment that his laboratory at Delco had not been able to do much of the pioneering kind of research he wanted to do—because of continual hindrance from current problems demanding solution—he determined to try again to set up a separate laboratory for research alone. That decision was important both because of the good results that came out of it directly and also because it became a link in the chain of circumstances that led him into still broader fields.

The bugbear of knock in the gasoline engine was the principal thing that caused him to make that decision. Twice this disturbance had bobbed up as an obstacle in his path. In his development of the Delco-Light plant, the violent knocking in the little engine which resulted when he had to use kerosine as fuel instead of gasoline had forced him to lower its compression and so cut down its output of power. Before that time, in his work on battery ignition, too, knock in the automobile engine had caused him much trouble.

It was about 1913 that the unpleasant metallic noise in engines called knock had begun to be an annoyance to automobile drivers. It came then because the increasing number of automobiles in use raised the demand for gasoline. Since that was before the advent of modern methods of refining, petroleum refiners met the rising demand mostly by distilling more of the crude oil into the gasoline fraction. That not only made the gasoline less volatile or harder to vaporize; it also increased the prevalence of knock in automobiles, to the great annoyance of those who drove them.

Magneto makers, in their fight against the rapid spread of Delco battery ignition, took advantage of that circumstance to blame battery ignition for having brought on that knocking in engines. Spark knock, they called it. Kettering demonstrated that the knock was not brought on by his battery ignition, but he nevertheless knew very little about it, and in characteristic fashion he determined to find out.

Now, it happened that during Kettering's development of the Delco-Light plant a young mechanical engineer, Thomas Midgley, Jr., had come to work for him. Young Midgley, then not long out of Cornell University, was to prove himself one of the most versatile and productive research men who ever worked with Kettering. Starting out as a mechanical engineer, Midgley was to make the most of his contributions in the field of chemistry, in the course of which he became a world-renowned research chemist and a man who won Kettering's high esteem. After Midgley's death in 1944, Kettering said of him, "He was like a brother to me."

On a certain Saturday afternoon in the late fall of 1916 Kettering sat down with Midgley and told him of those frustrating experiences he had had with knock in engines. He told Midgley that, because of the criticism of battery ignition, he had some time before that purchased an instrument, or indicator, for studying events in the engine cylinders. But the self-starter business had been growing so fast and bringing on so many problems that he had found no time at all to use the indicator. It had been put away in a closet.

"Why don't you go to my office," Kettering now suggested to Midgley, "get out that box, put the indicator on a Delco-Light engine and see what you can find out about knock?" Kettering later said, "It took a whole Saturday afternoon to sell Midge on the idea that this was quite an important project." But he succeeded so well in exciting Midgley's interest that for several years thereafter the young man worked on the problem in intensive fashion. For Midgley, those years proved to be like a story out of *The Arabian Nights*.

Midgley first set up a little engine and built a beaver-board enclosure around it. The object was to shut out light well enough to use the optical indicator and to photograph the cards it gave. "The first pictures of pressure events in the engine cylinder we made on Saturday afternoon by a very improvised method," Kettering recalled. "We took two little pieces of lath, two shingle nails, and a tomato can. Out of those parts we made a film drum which could be rotated— by hand—in the path of the beam of light from the indicator. We wrapped a piece of photographic paper around the tomato-can drum and secured it with rubber bands. Then, with the engine running, I spun the tomato can on its shingle-nail pivots and Midgley operated the shutter of the indicator." It was by that makeshift means that the first photographic records of knocking events in an engine were secured. And those records yielded this important item of information: knock does not come from preignition, as was then commonly supposed. It is an abrupt and violent rise in pressure which comes *after* ignition by the spark plug.

Speculating then on why kerosine knocked worse than gasoline, as it was known to do, the two men reasoned that it might be because kerosine did not vaporize as readily as gasoline. They recalled that the wild flower, the trailing arbutus, with its red-backed leaves, blooms early in the spring, even under snow. If only kerosine were dyed red, they speculated, it might—like the leaves of the trailing arbutus— absorb heat faster, and so vaporize quickly enough to burn in the engine like gasoline.

Midgley went to the chemical laboratory to see whether he could get a red dye for that purpose. But none was available. However, the young chemist, Fred L. Chase, who happened to be in the laboratory then, pulled down from the shelf a bottle of iodine with the suggestion that iodine ought to dye kerosine red. And when Midgley ran his little engine on kerosine made red with that iodine, sure enough, the knock *was* reduced greatly! The theory was thus apparently confirmed.

But when soon afterward kerosine reddened with a regular dye was run there was no effect whatever on the knock, no matter how deep the dye. Nevertheless, out of that mistaken notion came the important discovery that knock is suppressed by a minute amount of iodine. Because iodine is scarce and because it reacts and damages fuel to which it is added, it could not be put into gasoline in a practical way, but it showed that a powerful suppresser of knock did exist.

"The destruction of a theory is of no consequence," said Kettering later, "for theories are only steppingstones. More great scientific developments have been made by stumbling than by what is thought of as science. . . . In my opinion an ounce of experimentation is worth a pound of theory."

"It was about this time," Kettering recalled, "that we sat down and discussed what should be done. Midgley was under the impression that we should get a chemist and put him on the job. I told him that I thought we had better go a little farther in the analysis of the problem ourselves before we tried to get any specialists, because this was a subject which undoubtedly nobody knew anything about; and, if we brought in specialists, they would try to make the problem that we were working on conform to known facts. I said: 'This is like a group of fellows who are going on a long trip and don't want to start out with packs on their backs which contain a lot of things they will not use. . . . Let's you and me go up and survey the road first without any packs on our backs.' "

This was about the end of 1916, and Kettering felt that

it was now time to set up a separate research laboratory for the study, first of all, of fuels and how they burn in engines. He happened to know a man who, he thought, would be just the person to organize the new research laboratory he had in mind, Dr. F. O. Clements. This was the man who, when Kettering was a student at Ohio State, had been his laboratory instructor in freshman chemistry. Later, at Kettering's suggestion, Dr. Clements was persuaded to come from the laboratory of the Union Pacific Railroad at Omaha to the National Cash Register Company. There he set up and operated an experimental and control laboratory and there the acquaintanceship of the two men was renewed.

Dr. Clements accepted Kettering's invitation to organize a new research laboratory for him. Thus began a still closer association between the two men, which extended until the retirement of Dr. Clements in 1939. Throughout that period, Dr. Clements, a self-effacing man with thick white hair and eminent capabilities, performed a great service for Kettering, particularly in directing the organizational and personnel side of his extensive research endeavors.

"I told Dr. Clements," said Kettering, "that what we should do was to set up an organization as a means of studying, from various angles and without any immediate industrial implications, the application of fuel to an engine. 'Let's treat it,' I said, 'as our intellectual golf game, because I am sure that we will have to do a great deal of work before this will crystallize into usable form.' " Speaking later to the members of the Society of Automotive Engineers about what he had then called his "golf game," he said, "I don't think we used the same proportion of profanity as is used in that game."

The iodine discovery had been made in an old building that had been a tobacco warehouse—a building that did not even have running water. However, as Kettering has said, "A problem is not solved in a laboratory. It is solved in some fellow's head. All the apparatus is for is to get his head turned around so that he can see the thing right."

Nevertheless, what Dr. Clements set out to provide was a laboratory with facilities more adequate to do research on fuel problems and others in which Kettering was interested than was then available, and especially one free from the interruptions so unavoidable in a laboratory that is part of a manufacturing concern. An old mansion at 127 North Ludlow Street in Dayton, Ohio, was found to be available and it was decided to fit it up as a laboratory. But by that time— it was then about the middle of 1917—the United States had joined the Allies in waging World War I. As soon as the new laboratory could be fitted out, it began therefore to be devoted altogether to research bearing on the war effort.

Because of Kettering's active mind, his diversified experience, and his intense desire to help, he was dragged into many activities during World War I. He had trouble keeping from being pulled into too many. Two major projects centered in the laboratory he had just founded. The first was the effort to get a better—more knock-free—gasoline for use in the Liberty airplane engine. The other was the development of a flying robot bomb—or "aerial torpedo," as it was called.

Knock, the same power thief with which Kettering was familiar, showed up in the Liberty engine and put a limit on its output of power. And in aerial combat high performance is vital. Because it has always been Kettering's habit to talk freely to everyone about what he is doing in research, it had become known that he and Midgley had been studying knock as an obstacle to engine power. They were therefore asked to help find a means of eliminating knock in the Liberty airplane engine.

With characteristic enthusiasm they dived into the effort to find a better gasoline for the Liberty engine, one that would be free enough from knock to permit the engine to have higher compression and so to give a larger output of power. Some men from the U.S. Bureau of Mines collaborated in this endeavor also, notably E. W. Dean, Clarence Netzen, and John P. Smootz.

Gasolines were first collected from many places, in the United States and abroad, and tested for knock in a one-cylinder adaptation of the Liberty engine in which the compression ratio could be varied. It was found that gasoline obtained from certain California crude oils was much freer from knock than the Pennsylvania gasoline then being used in airplane engines. That California gasoline would have permitted the compression of the Liberty engine to have been boosted by one full ratio, thus giving a big increase in engine power. It was accordingly suggested that California gasoline be used as fuel for airplanes flown in combat.

But, unfortunately, there was a wartime committee which turned down that recommendation as not practical. It was this frustrating experience, and several others which Kettering had with committees acting on progressive ideas, that caused him to say later, "If you want to iron a thing down to the most simple, commonplace, low form of mediocrity, get a committee to pick the flaws in it. Why? Because there isn't one man in a thousand who has imagination."

When ten years afterward Mrs. Kettering read about Lindbergh's solo flight across the Atlantic, she said to her husband, "How wonderful that he did it all alone!"

"It would have been still more wonderful," Kettering replied, "if he had done it with a committee."

However, as that first suggestion of theirs for getting a better aviation gasoline was turned down, Kettering and his men simply began to look for another solution. They were not at all disposed to give up the search because of a single setback.

As a means of getting the more knock-free fuel sought, it

was now proposed to make cyclohexane, a hydrocarbon thought to be somewhat like California gasoline in properties. This was to be done synthetically by adding hydrogen to benzene in the presence of nickel as a catalyst. Benzene, as a by-product of coking coal, was readily available then in quantity.

But this effort to hydrogenate benzene was also undertaken against advice that it was impracticable. Leo H. Baekeland, famous chemist, inventor of the photographic paper Velox and of the pioneer plastic Bakelite, and at that time a member of the Naval Consulting Board headed by Thomas A. Edison, told Kettering that he would give him a wooden medal if he and his men could make a pint of cyclohexane. Kettering knew Dr. Baekeland well, because Delco, as a maker of ignition systems, was one of the first large users of Bakelite. Dr. Baekeland perhaps did not know that telling Kettering a thing could not be done was very likely to make him want to try it. And it happened that way this time. Fortunately, after a great deal of effort and a good many failures, it was found that benzene could be hydrogenated successfully. Thus was made the first synthetic aviation gasoline, a mixture of cyclohexane and benzene.

By present standards—standards not yet in existence back there—that first synthetic aviation gasoline had an octane number of 75 at lean, or cruising, fuel-air ratio and about 100 at rich, or take-off, mixture. Those values are to be compared with a rating of only 50 to 55 octane number for the aviation gasoline of that time, whether at lean mixture ratio or rich. The new fuel would thus have made possible a big boost in the power of the Liberty airplane engine; but the Armistice came before it could be put to use in practice.

As for Dr. Baekeland and his prediction of failure, a pint bottle of the first cyclohexane made in the endeavor was presented to him with proper ceremony, together with a proposed design for the wooden medal he had promised. The latter was in the form of a humorous diagram, a benzene ring surrounded by cats, to suggest cat-alysis. The outcome was so pleasing to Dr. Baekeland that that bottle of cyclohexane became one of his prized possessions, and he kept it on his desk for a long time. For his own experience in research had taught him, as he said, "to bow humbly before the facts, even if they do not seem to agree with my favorite theories."

The success in making cyclohexane in the face of the prediction that it was not possible was just one of the experiences that caused Kettering to hold the philosophy which he sometimes expressed thus: "We find that in research a certain amount of intelligent ignorance is essential to progress; for, if you know too much, you won't try the thing."

In looking for ways to expend machines rather than men against the enemy, the military people came up, early in World War I, with a scheme for a small pilotless and expendable bombing airplane. The idea called for a plane that could carry about 300 pounds of explosive, that could fly 50 miles or more under its own controls, and that could be sent with reasonable accuracy to bomb a given spot. That plan was brought to Kettering by Brigadier General George O. Squier, head of the Signal Corps, with the request that he assume charge of developing suitable means of putting it into effect. Kettering accepted the assignment.

The problem of such a robot bombing plane divided itself into three compartments: power plant, controls for direction and altitude, and airplane proper, or the "kite," as it was called. The design and development of the kite Kettering delegated chiefly to the men in the experimental engineering department of the Dayton-Wright Airplane Company. This was a company engaged in making airplanes for use in the war, and of which Kettering was an officer. The men from that department who were chiefly concerned with the kite for the aerial torpedo were Jay M. Schoonmaker, Jr., chief engineer, and designers Louis C. Luneke and Roland V. Hutchinson.

The development of the power plant, which was to be a small gasoline engine simple in design and cheap to build, was assigned to C. H. Wills, who had been chief engineer of the Ford Motor Company. Wills was assisted by Ralph De Palma, famed race driver.

The development of the most difficult feature of all—the automatic controls for direction, altitude, and distance of flight—Kettering put in charge of Thomas Midgley, Jr.; but to it he devoted much of his personal attention also. Since that was before the day of electronics, the miraculous schemes of the present day for guiding missiles were not known. Direction of flight was therefore controlled by means of a fast-spinning gyroscope, developed as a special adaptation of the gyroscopic compass. Altitude was regulated by means of an aneroid barometer, and distance by means of an air log.

The gyroscope and the aneroid could not of themselves provide the force for moving the controls of the little plane, of course. That power was furnished by pneumatic elements, air bellows, similar to those used in pipe organs and player pianos, and these were actuated by suction from the crankcase of the little engine. Kettering recalled that he got the first of those bellows by "pinching pieces out of my pipe organ and my player piano."

There was an advisory board to help guide the aerial torpedo project. On that board were Orville Wright, Robert A. Millikan, Elmer A. Sperry, Sr., Colonel Bion J. Arnold, and others. Among the many men who helped with the aerial torpedo was a young member of the Aviation Section of the Signal Corps, Colonel H. H. Arnold. This was the same H. H. Arnold who was Commanding General of the U.S. Army

Air Forces in World War II, and who afterward was made General of the Air Force (5-star).

At last came the time when flight trials of the aerial torpedo were to be made. In the first of these the little plane took off as planned and climbed steeply to about 150 feet. But there it whip-stalled, turned, and, on its way to a crash landing, dived dangerously at the groups of men assembled.

On hand for the second trial flight, besides Kettering and most of the civilians concerned with the development, were General Squier, Colonel Bion J. Arnold, and Colonel H. H. Arnold. It was a fine summer evening. But, unfortunately, the little plane misbehaved again. Launched successfully in the still evening air, it circled the field a few times. Then it disappeared behind a patch of clouds, flying toward the east in the general direction of the town of Xenia.

That was definitely not according to plan, for the aerial torpedo was a secret project and was intended to land right there on the test field. Several of the men set out posthaste in search of the little plane. After a time they came upon the wreckage in a field near Xenia. The farmers in the vicinity had seen the plane crash and were searching everywhere for the pilot. To set their minds at rest, Colonel Bion J. Arnold told the searchers a white lie, as he pointed to Colonel H. H. Arnold: "There's the pilot. He bailed out with a parachute."

Later other and more successful flights were made. Soon the aerial torpedo was judged successful enough for manufacture of the units to begin. That part of the program was in charge of Charles Lee, an expert in making experimental products, who had first worked for Kettering at the National Cash Register Company.

Then in the late summer of 1918, Colonel H. H. Arnold was ordered to go to France and make the necessary preparations for putting the aerial torpedo into combat. He sailed with complete plans and tactical studies. But that was the year of the great influenza epidemic. On the way across Colonel Arnold was stricken and spent some time in a hospital in Southampton. Thus it was that, by the time he reached France and reported to General Pershing, the Armistice had been declared. He remembered that General Pershing said to him then: "Young man, that is a very important development. I would keep at work on that, because you will need it in the next war."

When World War II did come, the then General H. H. Arnold, Commander of the U.S. Air Forces, said in a speech at Detroit that at the outset of the war he and Kettering and William S. Knudsen, serving then as director general of the Office of Production Management, had discussed the question of using a robot plane against the Germans. But the decision was against it, he said, largely because the targets were too far distant from any base of ours. They could be reached best by means of bombing planes with men as pilots. But that that decision had to be made was a cause of regret to both Kettering and General Arnold.

During World War I Kettering had a small part also in the development of the two-way wireless telephone for communication between airplane and ground. As a former telephone man, that wireless telephone was interesting to Kettering, and his agile mind leaped to its future possibilities. Addressing the Knife and Fork Club of Kansas City just after the war, he predicted that soon, simply by turning knobs on a little box, people would be able to get music and news right out of the air.

After the address, one of those present said to him, "I enjoyed your talk very much, and, until you injected that wireless story into it, I thought it was very practical. But now I am disappointed because everybody knows that can't be done."

When four or five years later Kettering spoke in Kansas City again, one of those who talked to him afterward said: "You won't remember me, I suppose, but I am the fellow who when you were here before told you that I didn't believe what you said about radio. I want to apologize for what I said then, for I have a radio now, although I can't really believe it yet."

Glad to see the end of World War I, Kettering plunged enthusiastically into peacetime research again. He was now nearing a new phase of his career, with a wider field of activity and influence.

Soon after World War I Kettering made up his mind to learn to fly an airplane himself. And B. L. (Benny) Whelan, then a pilot for the Dayton-Wright Airplane Company and now general manager of Sikorsky Aircraft, undertook to teach him. Kettering was a different student from any other he had ever taught, Whelan remembers, in that he came nearest to knowing how to pilot a plane beforehand. What he needed most was some practice. Of actual instruction he required only a very little.

For a long period after learning to fly Kettering used to get up early and take his plane into the air, which he did in many kinds of weather. In fact, he went up to study the weather and air currents. He would keep his plane sitting out, waiting for word from the Weather Bureau, which he had asked to let him know when there was to be some special weather, such as when it was going to hail.

Nevertheless, he was a careful flier, one who did not do any stunting. "There is just as much sense to stunting in an airplane," he said once, "as there is to running down the street, putting on the brakes and skidding around the corner. . . . I have always had a rule for myself: Never fly when the birds don't, because they have had a lot of experience."

In the summer of 1919 he and Howard Rinehart made a nonstop flight from Dayton to Wichita, Kansas, a distance of about 800 miles. Although not made official, that flight was a record for the time. "We did not come from Dayton to Wichita by air to try a stunt," said Kettering in a speech he made there on that occasion, "but because the modern airplane is capable of making the trip and because people did not know that such a thing could be done."

"I made only two railroad trips last year," he said in 1920. "I flew more than 15,000 miles. I was not out joy riding. I was just at one place and wanted to go somewhere else, and I traveled in an airplane. Several years hence the aircraft industry will be a big business. It is in its infancy, but it is developing. . . . A means of transportation three to five times faster than any other is a utility. It is such a great utility that we do not at first appreciate it."

Even in those years around 1920, before flying aids or even landing fields, he was flying everywhere, and sometimes most informally. Benny Whelan remembers a time when Kettering's secretary, Charlie Adams, called him and said, "Boss Ket wants to go to St. Marys, Ohio. Will you please fly him up?"

When the time came, Kettering got into the plane and Whelan took off for St. Marys. There was no landing field at St. Marys, but the landmark for the town was the lake to the west of it. Arriving over St. Marys, Whelan found a field that looked all right, set the plane down, and taxied it to the corner nearest the town.

It was then that Boss Ket said to him, "Benny, do you know why I came up here? What did Charlie tell you? I have forgotten just what I am supposed to do here."

But at that point a group of men, who knew he was going

to fly there and had been looking for his plane, came up. From them it was learned that he was to be the guest speaker that evening at a meeting of the Idlewild Club.

Kettering was one of the pioneers in improving the airplane and techniques of flying. Soon after he began flying he substituted a fuel pump for the pressure fuel system used on early airplanes, a dangerous feature of planes at that time. He was one of the first instrument fliers. In his plane he had a row of instruments, even though regular fliers at that time called it an old man's plane and said that anybody who used instruments in flying was a "sissy."

About flying under conditions of bad visibility, Kettering once remarked to another pilot in his roguish way, "If you should ever be in doubt throw out a monkey wrench. If it goes up, you are flying upside down. If it goes down, you are flying right side up."

He was an early advocate of radio-marked airplane routes and other aids to flying. "When we get this radio-marking across the country," he said years ago, "it will be possible to take an airplane equipped with some new compass devices we already have and some other little trinkets developed during the war, put it on a course from Chicago to Dayton, and turn the flying of it over to the compass, which will do it better than we could anyway."

After World War I an experimental airplane was built under Kettering's guidance and sponsorship which had an all-cantilever wing structure. This was probably the first United States plane to have a practical retractable landing gear. Also, it was equipped with wing flaps which were possibly the first of the high-lift devices. This plane is now in the Edison Museum at Dearborn, Michigan.

It was in connection with the building of that airplane that an event occurred especially revealing of Kettering's profound absorption in the development of new products. Part of the plan was to fly that airplane in the Gordon Bennett Race in France. As the date of the race drew near, the pressure on getting the plane completed was intensified. The mechanism for actuating the wing flaps, a train of gears and shafts enclosed in wings covered completely with a skin of wood veneer, was not operating as it ought.

One evening while the men were working, Kettering and Mrs. Kettering drove up on their way to the theater. He wanted to see first just how the men were getting along. He was dressed in his tuxedo. Some of the men were up on the wing, their shoes off to avoid scarring the surface, working on the mechanism. Kettering kicked off his shoes and got up there, too, to work on the mechanism himself and to see what he could do with it. Soon he took off his coat and dropped it over the wing. A little later he reached into the pocket of his vest, took out the theater tickets, and said to Mrs. Kettering: "Here, Mother, you had better take these tickets. Ernest will drive you on to the theater. I'll have to stay here."

PART III

Yesterday, Today, and Tomorrow

1920–

Kettering (center) in typical posture of experimentation during the early days of the self-starter.

Kettering had an active interest in events at Triangle Park, conducted by and for the people of Delco. Louis Ruthenberg of Delco (left), and G. Walter Spahr (center).

1912 Cadillac on w[...]
the electric self-starter
peared first.

With three men of particular importance in Kettering's early auto-
mobile career. From the left, J. B. Edwards, president, Kellogg
Switchboard and Supply Company; W. A. Chryst, chief engineer of
Delco; Henry Leland, president of Cadillac; and Kettering.

With the first electric sel[...]
starter and the control mechan[...]
ism for it. Photographed on th[...]
occasion of Kettering's 75t[...]
birthday.

XIII

IN THE SUMMER OF 1919, just a few months after the close of World War I, events which were to widen the field of Kettering's activity and influence began to take shape. The men guiding the affairs of General Motors Corporation decided to provide further facilities for improving the products they then had and for developing new products by establishing a central research laboratory in Detroit. Casting about for a man of outstanding ability and with experience in research to head such a laboratory, they were all of the opinion that—as it was then recorded by the secretary—"Mr. Kettering is by far the most valuable man known to this corporation for the position."

The members of the General Motors policy group which made that decision included Pierre S. du Pont, chairman of the board; W. C. Durant, president; John J. Raskob, chairman of the Finance Committee; and vice-presidents Alfred P. Sloan, Jr., and Walter P. Chrysler. Sloan in particular recognized Kettering as just the kind of man being sought to help build General Motors.

But when Kettering was invited to take that important post he said no. He already had too many irons in the fire looking after his business interests and directing the researches he was then pursuing in the little laboratory in Dayton, he said.

Being very desirous of getting Kettering to devote his talents to General Motors, the group then came forward with a proposal to take over all his Dayton business interests under some suitable arrangement, and so to set him free to devote his full talents to research. That he did consent to do, but only under certain conditions. The first of those conditions was that the research laboratory be established not in Detroit but in Dayton, and with the little laboratory he already had there as a nucleus.

Another of his stipulations Kettering stated in these words: "I told Mr. Sloan that I would take it on three conditions—that I would have no responsibility and no authority, and that I would never be held accountable for the money I spent. I don't think you can run a research laboratory any other way. The minute you take responsibility or authority, you quit researching. You can't keep books on research, because you don't know when you are going to get anything out of it or what it is going to be worth when you get it."

The new research laboratory was set up in a large one-story building at Moraine City, six miles south of Dayton, where during the war airplanes had been made by the Dayton-Wright Airplane Company. The organization came to be called the General Motors Research Corporation. Kettering was the head of it, and Dr. F. O. Clements was his principal administrative assistant with the title of technical director.

In January, 1920, Kettering's place was enlarged further by making him a vice-president of General Motors Corporation. In December of that year he was elected a member of the board of directors also.

Kettering took up his new work with the enthusiasm characteristic of him. The laboratory was situated not far from Ridgeleigh Terrace, the Kettering home, and could be seen from it. Kettering's happiness in his new work was expressed by his father-in-law, Alonzo Williams, visiting at Ridgeleigh Terrace about that time, when he said to Carroll A. Hochwalt, a member of the research laboratory staff, "Charlie is mighty happy and thrilled at having this research laboratory. He bounds down the stairs in the morning three steps at a time. He looks out at the laboratory here in the valley below and is so enthusiastic about the place that he can hardly wait to get down to it."

Just before the formation of the General Motors Research Corporation, two principal research endeavors were being pursued in the little laboratory of which Kettering was head. These now became principal projects in the new and larger laboratory. The first was a search for a better and more practical knock-suppressing agent than iodine, the effect of which had been discovered just before the war. The second endeavor, an altogether new one, was the effort to develop an air-cooled engine using copper fins. In this copper-cooling project the plan was to take the copper used in the radiator of an automobile and to put it right on the cylinders of the engine in the form of fins to be cooled with air blown over the fins by a fan.

The idea of air-cooling did not originate with Kettering, but he felt that by proper development of copper finning he could make an important contribution to the cooling of automobile engines. He wanted to get better cooling and at the same time to do away with the need to use water, which often boiled in summer and had to be treated with antifreeze in winter.

During the first four years of the new General Motors Research Corporation this copper-cooled engine development was the major project pursued there. The decision of the General Motors officials to invite Kettering to head research for the corporation had in fact been based in some part upon "the air-cooled engine . . . and the possible future thereof."

The copper-cooling scheme was, under Kettering's enthusiastic guidance, pursued in intensive fashion. Various modifications and models were designed, built, and tested. Experiments were made on fans for effective cooling. An automatic machine for forming the copper fins into a strip of loops and cutting off the right amount to circle the cylinder was developed, as well as a commercial process and furnace for brazing the copper fins to the iron cylinder.

The work soon evolved into an effort to develop not only a copper-cooled engine but also a complete car which was to have been a replacement for the Chevrolet. Emphasis was on lightness and on the lowest possible cost of manufacture.

As always, Kettering was everywhere in person, adding his fire and energy to each part of the endeavor. Naturally, a great deal of engine testing was done. One night Kettering, wearing his dress suit, came to the laboratory from the theater, where he had been with Mrs. Kettering. An engine being tested on the dynamometer stand had just developed some internal trouble. The men had dropped the oil pan for an inspection. Dress suit and all, Kettering insisted on getting underneath the engine on his back holding a light, while oil dripped down on him, to see for himself what the trouble was. When he came out from under that engine, his clothes were, as one of the men said, "a sight to behold." But with complete unconcern about that, he said, "I found the trouble all right."

An immense amount of road testing of the copper-cooled cars was done, and Kettering took an active part in that also. Many of the testing tours were at his suggestion organized to be conducted over weekends. Often the cavalcade of test cars was accompanied by a light truck carrying blankets, cooking utensils, and other equipment for camping out, for that was what was usually done at night. In the party also were likely to be such a man as W. A. Chryst or Vice-President C. S. Mott—or even, on one occasion, the then president of General Motors, Pierre S. du Pont.

On such trips Kettering was an admirable fellow, recalls O. T. Kreusser, who had a part in them. He would shift from car to car and do most of the driving of the car in which he was riding. When roadside repairs had to be made—and many did have to be made—he was usually the one who decided what to do and how. Also, he often helped do it.

Kettering was the first man up in the morning. He would go out exploring to inspect the wildlife and the vegetation in the vicinity. It was characteristic of him to be interested in everything in nature—vegetation, living creatures, or whatever came to his attention.

Once while Kettering was driving a test car in the hills of Kentucky he got lost. Fred Davis was with him at the time, and he remembers that when they came upon a native of the region Kettering asked, "Can you tell us how to get to Cincinnati?"

"We-el," drawled the fellow uncertainly, "you go on up here to the fork of the road, and there you turn . . . Let's see, there you turn . . . Hang it all, mister, if I was goin' to Cincinnati, I wouldn't start from here!"

Kettering sometimes related that experience to emphasize the fact that, when doing research in industry, one must of course start from the place where one is, however unfavorable it may appear to be.

Another time Harry Collins was riding in a test car with Kettering, who was driving it just as hard as he could. They topped a knoll and there right before them were several ducks waddling across the road. At that Kettering just steered the car off the road and, after some violent bouncing, with Collins holding on as best he could, it came to rest in a plowed field with a broken spring.

"What in the world did you do that for?" Collins blurted out.

"Those ducks," Kettering replied. "We can get the car fixed. But I was a farmer once and I know what it would mean to lose all those ducks."

It may seem strange that, with all his responsibilities and

with as much capable help as he had, Kettering should have devoted so much of his own time to road testing. It was done in the exercise of his belief that it is a mistake for any man engaged in research to leave the practicing of it altogether to others. "It takes personal practice to drive delusions out of a fellow's mind," he said.

In illustration of this belief, he once told this story: "I was running some tests off the coast of Florida in connection with automatic steering devices for small boats, and when the weather was bad I used to work out there every day from about nine in the morning until three or four in the afternoon. The tests had to be run in bad weather because we couldn't find out anything in good weather.

"Some friends of mine down there for a vacation said: 'We think you are crazy, running that little boat up and down in the stormy Gulf Stream all day long. Why don't you get somebody to do that for you?'

"One of those men happened to be a very good golfer and the other an excellent violinist. So I said, 'I'll tell you what I'll do. You fellows get somebody to play your golf game for you and to practice your fiddle for you. If you find that that works, let me know, and I will get somebody to ride that boat for me. Right now I do not know how anybody else could get my firsthand experience for me.' "

After many months of effort, the copper-cooled car was considered developed to the stage at which manufacture of it by Chevrolet could be begun. William S. Knudsen was chosen as the person to put the new car into production.

The manufacture got under way at the Chevrolet factory in Flint around the end of 1922. It was carried on until about 3,000 of the copper-cooled cars had been delivered to customers. But at that point the making of the cars was stopped, and those already in the hands of customers were called back and replaced with the conventional water-cooled model.

The reasons for that decision were complex. In some part they were concerned with shortcomings in the new copper-cooled car itself, for all the development problems had not yet been thoroughly solved when the car was put into production. In part also they were the result of what Kettering considered unwarranted modifications introduced by those who made the production design and of imperfections in the manufacturing process.

But in large part the decision was based on other considerations. Important among these was opposition to the copper-cooled car by the general managers and chief engineers of the car-making divisions, who thought the introduction of it was too radical and uncertain a step to take at the time. In the end, in spite of the logical arguments in favor of copper-cooling and of all the immense amount of work done to develop an embodiment of the principle, the opinions of the managers and chief engineers of the car-making divisions won out. Thus it was that, although the copper-cooling project had cost many millions of dollars, it was abandoned altogether.

Coming as it did so early in the period of Kettering's activity in large-scale research, the discontinuance of the copper-cooled Chevrolet in the summer of 1923 was a staggering blow to him. It was then that his spirits reached the lowest point in his research career. Dr. F. O. Clements said that that was the only time he ever saw him completely discouraged.

So altogether disheartened was Kettering then that he asked Alfred P. Sloan, Jr., who shortly before had succeeded Pierre S. du Pont as president of General Motors, to relieve him as head of the Research Laboratories "at as early a date as possible." The circumstance that made his discouragement so deep was that he did not consider the copper-cooled engine a failure. The fundamental principles involved were so sound, he thought, that it could have been not a failure at all but a signal success.

He was not relieved as head of research for General Motors, of course. Instead, he went on from there to make large contributions to the success of the corporation. But it was in part his disheartening experiences in the copper-cooling development that made him say later that in research one of the first requirements is that "you must not bruise easily."

Kettering had told Sloan that, in spite of the fate of his major project, he felt that enough had come out of other researches being pursued in the new laboratory to pay for its existence. And in that he was quite right.

One of these was air-cooling for the domestic refrigerator. Immediately after World War I and before his laboratory had been amalgamated with General Motors, Kettering had begun experiments in that field. He wanted to make the electric refrigerator a portable apparatus that needed only to be plugged into a socket. He wanted at the same time to put an end to the water troubles that were a persistent and vexatious problem with the domestic refrigerator of that period. One of the men who worked with him on that endeavor at the Research Laboratories and who later went to Frigidaire, where the results of their years of experimentation were applied in practice, to the great improvement of the domestic refrigerator, was S. M. Schweller, who afterward became chief engineer of Frigidaire.

With the coming of the closed automobile body, freedom from vibration in the engine was of major importance. This was particularly so in the case of Cadillac, with its more fussy customers. Engine vibration produced by the conventional "flat crankshaft" in the Cadillac V-eight engine set up an objectionable drumming sound in closed bodies. Ernest Seaholm, chief engineer of Cadillac, had come to the Research Laboratories in search of a solution. By putting their heads together, R. V. Hutchinson and T. P. Chase of the staff there came up with the idea of a 90-degree "twisted" crankshaft

llow Street mansion, ~ton, Ohio, in which in 7 Kettering set up a oratory to do pioneer- research. This labora- y was the nucleus und which he later or- ized the General Motors Research Corporation.

The Engineers' Club of Dayton. Dedicated in 1918, this home was a gift to the club by Kettering and E. A. Deeds.

Father and son in chateristic attitudes of na study. The time was gust, 1921, when son G was thirteen.

The head men of Delco in the early years of the company take a little outing. From the left, W. A. Chryst, W. P. Anderson, Kettering, E. A. Deeds.

Road test caravan ready to set forth in August, 1921, on one of the many testing tours during the development of the copper-cooled engine. At the extreme right with Kettering beside him is C. S. Mott, vice-president of General Motors.

with counterweights. That idea, when worked out through a lot of experimentation, accomplished the purpose of quieting the Cadillac car in good style. Seaholm considered this development one of the biggest improvements in the Cadillac engine up to that time.

That new Cadillac crankshaft was the beginning of a series of important developments in the Research Laboratories, which eliminated vibration in the engines of all General Motors cars. It was about this time that C. E. Summers began there the development of one of these, the device which came to be called the "harmonic balancer." By effectively damping the twisting, or torsional, vibration of crankshafts, that device became a major factor in taking out of automobile engines the shiver and quake they had always had. The soothing of that vexatious shiver not only made driving much more pleasant; it also improved the durability of automobile engines and helped to make possible the faster turning and more powerful engines which came on afterward.

With the swing to closed automobile bodies after World War I, a faster drying finish than paint—and a more durable one—was urgently needed, too. It was taking two weeks or more to finish a car body; and, when some thousands of bodies were being built every day, the paint shop to house all of them during the finishing process was becoming excessively large. Kettering had, therefore, put on an intensive drive for the development of a finish that would be both faster drying and more durable than paint. With characteristic daring, he told a gathering of paint suppliers that it ought to be possible to finish an automobile body in an hour instead of two weeks.

The outcome of his campaign, and of much research done meanwhile in cooperation between H. C. Mougey and his group in the Research Laboratories, who worked on problems of application and tests of durability, and men in the du Pont Company, who worked on composition, was a fast-drying and durable lacquer finish which represented one of the great advances in automobile technology. That new and better finish first began to be put on cars commercially in the fall of 1923, the same year that the copper-cooled Chevrolet was discontinued.

Meanwhile the search that Kettering had started for an agent to eliminate knock as a barrier to higher engine power and better fuel economy was being pursued in the laboratory with great intensity. That investigation, the full story of which is told in a later chapter, was headed by Thomas Midgley, Jr. By the time the copper-cooled Chevrolet was discontinued, the commercial application of that development had been begun in a small way, and it later grew to huge proportions and importance.

These were just a few of the undertakings which, in spite of the failure of the copper-cooling project, made highly productive the endeavors Kettering was pursuing in the General Motors Research Corporation during the early period of its existence. Those accomplishments turned out to be much more important, in fact, than he or anyone else could foresee at that early time. They were thus a worthy beginning to the long series of advances to come out of research fostered by Kettering—achievements which made him "by far the most valuable man known to this corporation for the position."

During this period many members of the General Motors staff and others who visited the Research Laboratories were entertained at the Kettering home. Ernest Seaholm remembers that that was a most unusual experience when so many people were around with the free run of the place. Mrs. Kettering was a charming hostess, he said. She went out of her way to entertain that flood of visitors, sometimes under difficult circumstances. William S. Knudsen recalled that for the entertainment of her guests Mrs. Kettering used to play the pipe organ in the home. And Knudsen remarked upon what an excellent organist she was, particularly in playing the classical music he loved.

It was during these years, too, that Gene Kettering was coming up to young manhood. As he grew older, his father bought mechanical articles for him, including automobiles. And it was always understood that those were for Gene to take apart and to experiment with as he liked. Radio was just coming in then, and Gene and his father built radio sets together. They had a lot of fun doing it, and it all furthered Gene's interest and his education in practical things and how they are made.

About such things, things that he could get his hands on and experiment with, Gene learned readily and with understanding. But school proved difficult for him in many respects, partly at first because he did not take as much interest in it nor work as hard at it as he might have. This worried his father, who tried his best to correct it.

When Gene was away at summer camp, his father wrote to him frequently and urged Gene to write often to him. In his letters, along with news from home, the older Kettering from time to time included items such as these:

I hope you are having a good time and will drop me a card every day . . . it is bad taste to scratch a word on a card or letter . . . I am going to keep tab on the number of badly spelled words. . . . This last letter is very much better than any other you have written, but it still shows a little raggedness that I would like for you to improve on. . . . You said that you were going to be home on Saturday, August 36. I have looked through all of our calendars here and can find none that has more than 31 days in August. . . . Keep right on having a good time and when you come back make up your mind that you are going to lick this school business to a standstill.

In one of the several letters of encouragement Kettering wrote to Gene at college he said:

You have to add, as we do in business, your . . . assets and liabilities. It seems to me that your asset column is way above your liability. In the first place, you are very much interested in engineering, you have no difficulty in seeing through mechanisms and knowing what to do to fix them. You do not have to worry, as I did, about your finances. So all this has to be stacked up against the liability of your dislike for the mathematics that seem to be so essential in the modern engineering school. . . . I think the fact that you do not care to go out and bum around is decidedly in your favor. Physically, you are sound. If you could remove this one bugaboo, it looks to me as though you would have everything the way you want it.

And that is how it did come out in the end; for his father and mother succeeded in implanting in Gene high principles, a democratic attitude, a deep sense of responsibility, and a love of labor. It is Kettering's belief that a sense of personal responsibility is one of the most important things for a person to learn—responsibility for his job, for his family, and for the welfare of the community. He himself has that feeling in generous measure, and while Gene was growing up he and Mrs. Kettering succeeded in imparting it to him, too.

In the summer of 1924 the Ketterings were ready to leave Dayton for New York to sail the next day for Europe. Just before they were to take the train that August afternoon, they were visited by officials of the Winters National Bank and Trust Company and other citizens of Dayton gravely concerned about the financial condition of the bank. They informed the Ketterings that it was essential that something be done quickly to change the bank's management and ownership. It was explained that appeals had been made to several community interests without success, and they were now asking the Ketterings to step into the management and ownership of the bank as public-spirited citizens of means.

Kettering protested that the last thing he wanted was to own a bank. And, besides, he was all packed to go to Europe.

But, as he was in position to prevent a catastrophe to the people who had their money deposited there, it looked as though doing so might be for him a civic duty. And he made it a rule to fulfill his obligation to the community whenever he felt he had one.

So he said to those men: "I'll tell you what I'll do. If you will assemble the bank stock concerned, put it into a locked box and give me the key, I'll have our men go through this thing. And, in case it turns out to be as you say, then when I get back I'll assume those obligations."

When some weeks later he returned and found that conditions at the bank were just as had been related to him, he sent for the bank examiner. To him Kettering said that he knew nothing about running a bank. But what he wanted to do, he said, was to arrange to operate the Winters Bank in such a way that it would fully meet the requirements of the examiner. When he had learned what those requirements were, he proceeded to put them into effect.

In the reorganization of the Winters National Bank and Trust Company, Kettering became chairman of the new Board of Directors. George B. Smith, who was in charge of financial matters for Kettering and also for E. A. Deeds, was made one of the directors. S. Rufus Jones, prominent and respected financial man in the city, was elected president of the bank. Walter H. J. Behm joined the staff of the bank at this time to become cashier. Later Walter Behm was for many years to serve the Winters Bank with distinction as its president.

In thus becoming a banker because of what he considered to be his obligation to the community, Kettering went against his own desires and also against the advice of some others. One of those who did not favor it was his own attorney, who said, "If Boss Ket persists in doing what he has been talking about he is going to lose every dollar he's got."

What the attorney did not know perhaps was just how little Kettering was concerned about losing his money. Someone asked him once, "Suppose you lost everything you have. What would you do?"

"Well," he replied, "I would do just what I did before when I didn't have any money. . . . I would create something people want, something they need, and would pay money for. . . . I'm not afraid of losing my assets, because I don't believe that a man's assets are in money."

In telling the members of the staff about his ideas and plans for the bank, Kettering said that he had no desire to be a financier. All he wanted was to operate as a real good honest country bank is run. He told them, too, that people must be treated with unvarying courtesy, for the bank has nothing to build on except courtesy and service.

He requested also that the bank try to be of service to people in financial matters in every way possible, even though the service was not always directly related to banking as usually considered. Every effort should be made to serve people, he said, whether or not it appeared that doing so would pay.

More than once he expressed in words such as these his views on the importance of prosperous business enterprises to successful banking: We have too long followed the bankers' definition of prosperity—bank balances and bank clearances. But these are the negative side of the circuit, because prosperity is measured by the flow of useful goods in the channels of trade. That must always go ahead of the return flow of money through the countinghouses. The bank clearances which follow are thus the negative phase of prosperity and the flow of useful materials is the positive.

In carrying out the policies Kettering set forth, the Winters Bank was later to become the largest financial institution in Dayton and one of the best of its size in the Middle West.

XIV

ONE OF THE MISTAKES Kettering made was his insistence that the General Motors Research Corporation be located not in Detroit but in Dayton. He soon found that Dayton was too far away from the people he was trying to serve. Most of them had headquarters in Detroit or nearby. The time required for them to get to Dayton and back was a serious hindrance to the personal contacts needed for the fullest success of his endeavors in their behalf. In 1925, therefore, much as Kettering disliked leaving Dayton, he moved the base of his operations to Detroit.

His home and what might be called his citizenship remained in Dayton, however. He and Mrs. Kettering took a suite of rooms in the Book-Cadillac Hotel (now the Sheraton-Cadillac) which served for more than twenty years as their Detroit residence. But as often as they could they returned to their Dayton home for short periods.

Out of those frequent trips from Detroit to Dayton came Kettering's celebrated Route 25 story. "My home is in Dayton," he would say. "But I can't get a job there. So I work in Detroit, and I have driven back and forth for years. It is about 220 miles. A friend of mine who makes the trip once in a while said to me, 'I understand you make that trip in four hours and a half.'

" 'Yes, I do,' I said.

" 'Well,' he replied, 'I'm a better driver than you, and I can't do it in that time.'

"So I asked him to go along with me one day. When we made the trip in just four hours and a half, he said, 'No wonder you can do it in that time. You don't stay on Route Twenty-five!' "

Often Kettering used that story to emphasize for young people and others the importance of getting off the beaten track, especially if one is to be successful in developing new things. "Invention," he would say, "is nothing more than getting off Route 25."

In Detroit the transplanted Research Laboratories were established partly in the General Motors Building in the heart of the city and partly three blocks away on Cass Avenue in what was called Building 9. This building had been part of the Cadillac factory fifteen years earlier when Kettering had begun his visits to that company. This arrangement continued for four years only. Then the laboratories were all moved into a new building constructed for the purpose across the street from the General Motors Building.

The researches which in this new location Kettering continued to foster and pursue so intensively were aimed at making the automobile easier to drive, more pleasant to ride in, more trouble-free, more durable, and more economical. He sometimes told a story of the man who said to him: "You fellows haven't done a new thing in the automobile business during the last twenty-five years."

"What makes you say that?" Kettering asked.

The man's answer was to show him the parts list of the 1912 Cadillac on which the self-starter had appeared, and by comparison the parts list of a current car. "Read those two lists," the critic said, "and you will see that both are about the same."

"But they are the same only in name," Kettering replied. "The proportionalities of those parts—the fitting one to another—the metallurgy, the steel, are all different. The paint is still paint, but it is different; the tires are still tires, but they are different. Despite the fact that the catalogue of parts has not been greatly changed, the progress through the years has made, for him who drives the car and for those who ride in it, a difference that is almost unbelievable."

Important aids in bringing about that difference were such products of the Research Laboratories as better bearings, better axle gears, better springs and actuating mechanisms for valves, long-lasting and trouble-free fan belts, better metals and alloys, means of eliminating the failure of parts from fatigue, and other improvements.

To all these and many others Kettering and the Research Laboratories he headed made contributions of great importance. They worked out means of quieting valve mechanisms and of silencing intake and exhaust noise; they improved brakes and lighting systems; they bettered the appearance and durability of plated parts; they greatly improved lubricants and lubrication systems; and they contributed to the development of two-way shock absorbers, safety glass, and automatic transmissions. Also, to make successful application of the means for taking vibration and quake out of automobiles, they developed machines for balancing rotating parts in production before they were assembled in place—not only crankshafts for engines, but also clutches, flywheels, propeller shafts, tire and wheel assemblies, and other parts to a total of about seventy.

As head of such a central research laboratory, one of Kettering's important functions, one in which he had preeminent ability, was that of selling the results of research—and, at the outset, research itself—to the practical engineers and executives in the manufacturing divisions. And that was seldom easy. Out of his experience Kettering has said that new ideas are the hardest things in the world to merchandise. Concerning one man with whom he had to deal, one who made it an invariable practice to resist change, Kettering suggested to the general manager of the man's division that he could better afford to pay him a good salary to stay away from the plant altogether than to let him remain in position to prevent new things from being done. "Just tell him that any time he comes nearer than a mile from the plant his salary will stop," Kettering suggested.

"The greatest durability contest in the world is getting a new idea into any factory," Kettering said. "I will defy any factory organization to lick me on the job. . . . They can kick me in the ribs or bat me in the eye, and I am perfectly unconscious of it, provided I know my idea is all right. . . . No one can say how many discoveries have been lost because the discoverers weren't tough enough to stick to their guns and make the world believe and accept."

However, Kettering believes in the inevitability of progress. He recalled a time, in the days of the Model T Ford, when Henry Ford told him that he was not going to put a self-starter on the Ford car. "Mr. Ford," Kettering replied, "that is something you yourself are not going to have anything to say about."

The effort to get still better and more durable finishes for cars was continued in active fashion after the move to Detroit. The men most active in that program were H. C. Mougey and R. J. Wirshing, both long-time members of the research staff.

Kettering not only took a great interest in that endeavor; he also made direct contributions of importance to it, especially in the instrumentation of exposure tests to measure durability. Because paint panels exposed in Florida showed much faster "weathering" or failure than in the North, a test field was established there which for many years has been headed by Earl M. De Noon.

It was supposed that the faster failure in Florida was caused by the magnificent Florida sunshine or by the greater amount of ultraviolet light. But when it was observed that paint panels exposed to the light of ultraviolet lamps in the laboratory did not give results that corresponded with outdoor exposure tests, Kettering set out to develop a sunlight recorder to find out just how much sun energy did fall on an exposure panel per day.

Then, in a variation of the program, panels were exposed at different hours of the day. As a consequence, it was observed that the paint films on panels put out only during the daytime did not fail as fast as those exposed twenty-four hours a day. This suggested that something other than sunshine, something happening at night, was a factor in the rapid failure of paint films.

Surmising that that factor might be dew, Kettering developed a dew meter. Later he developed also a modification of that instrument which indicated when a panel was wet with rain. The difference between the readings of the two meters thus gave the time when the panels were wet with dew. By these means the men established that it was a combination of the dew of nighttime and the sunshine of daytime that caused the rapid failure of paint films in Florida.

Much of Kettering's experimentation on car finishes was done in Florida at the General Motors Test Field near Miami. For many years he and Mrs. Kettering spent a few weeks of each winter in Florida. For Kettering it was a vacation, relief from winter in the North. Unlike some others, though, he did not go to Florida to play golf, fish, or loaf. Instead, most of his days were filled with some form of experimentation.

Although he was often absorbed in his experiments, he nevertheless had a good time in Florida. He enjoyed particularly the opportunities it gave him for association with his friends, so many of whom gathered there in winter—men such as Paul W. Litchfield, Carl G. Fisher, Gar Wood, John Oliver LaGorce, and Cyrus H. K. Curtis. During the later years of their visits to Florida, the Ketterings had a tower apartment at the Surf Club in Miami Beach—an apartment which the officers of the club had built for the exclusive use of them and their guests.

Some time after the new and better finishes for cars had become successfully established, Kettering was visited in his office by one of the paint suppliers. This man had been present earlier when Kettering has astounded a group of paint men by telling them that it ought to be possible to finish a car in an hour instead of two weeks. "I happened to have an ordinary paint color card lying on my desk," Kettering related, "and I said to this man—he had driven there in his automobile—'If you were having your car refinished today, what color would you have it done in?' After deliberating, and thinking whether his wife would like it or not, he picked out a certain color and we went to lunch. When we came back we sat around and talked for a while. Finally, he said, 'I'll have to be going.'

"He then looked out the window and exclaimed, 'My car is gone!'

" 'No, it isn't,' I said. 'That's your car out there. Didn't you tell me that was the color you would like? We just refinished your car while you were at lunch.' "

In addition to all Kettering did in the field of improving automobiles, he had a pre-eminent part as an effective advocate of continued advancement and of the importance of the part the yearly model has in such advance. "I was one of the fellows who fought and fought for years to keep the yearly model," he remarked.

There were critics of the system of yearly models, of course, those who said that you sell a man a new automobile this year and next year you bring out a new model and depreciate the value of the old one. To such persons Kettering would say, "We don't depreciate the value of the old one at all. Did we put a scratch on the paint of your car? Did we score a cylinder? . . . No, we did not touch your car. It is just as good a piece of transportation as it was. What we did was to appreciate your mind. We have simply elevated your mental idea of what an automobile should be."

It was at the introduction of new models by one car maker —a special celebration of twenty-five years of operation by that company—that Kettering first used his illustration of a car in a glass case. He did it to emphasize the circumstance that that year's car, fine as it was, was only one stage in a process of continual evolution. The speakers who preceded him had lauded the new car in extravagant terms, and the last of them had said that the company would never build a finer car.

"I followed him in my talk," Kettering related. "And I said I would like to have them pick out what they thought was the best one of the cars, put it in a glass case, seal it up, and print the price on the outside in gold letters like those on the front of banks. Now we'll come back next year and take a look at the car. It won't look so good then because there will be a new model out. We can't get the posted price for it now, so we'll put the price of two hundred dollars less on the glass case at the front. But this time we'll print it there not in gold but in whitewash. We'll keep on doing that each year. And what do you think we can get for that car at the end of fifteen years? It will be just as good as it was when we put it in the case, but the only man who will buy it is the junk dealer."

Kettering is opposed to standardizing anything that can be improved. "I have no objection to the standardizing of bolts and nuts and screws," he said, "but I do have a terrible obsession against the standardization of ideas." He said this, too: "Advancing waves of other people's progress sweep over the unchanging man and wash him out."

Throughout his career Kettering has had a special interest in advertising. He talked about advertising a great deal and often was invited to address gatherings of advertising men and businessmen. "I believe in advertising," he would say. "It can accomplish great things. . . . But advertising is a story about a product, and I don't believe you can write the story into the product unless it is there . . . you have got to vitalize your product."

In his view, the best way to do that is through research. "I can't see spending forty million dollars for advertising and a million for research," he said. "If you will give me ten of that forty, I will make the other thirty talk louder than if you had fifty million."

"Advertising experts are always striving toward some new appeal in their copy," he commented also. "Well, I say spread some of the newness of appeal into the product. For it is the monotony of the sameness of things offered for sale that discourages buying. . . . Just try writing your friend a letter once a week about your dog, and before a year is gone he will be so tired of hearing about that dog of yours that he is likely to come around and shoot it."

In further expression of his belief in the need for making a determined search for more knowledge in his field, Kettering said: "Where I work we keep ourselves harnessed to the idea that we still have everything to learn about automobiles, and that is just the simple truth. We don't even know what makes an automobile run. It is so simple to explain it by saying, you take a charge of gasoline and air into the cylinder and compress it and ignite it with a spark, and it explodes and pushes the piston down, and that makes your car go. . . .

"If you stop right there, it is a logical explanation. But what does the spark do? What do you mean by combustion? We don't know why or how the spark sets off that explosion of gas. . . . So I say, quite solemnly, that we haven't the slightest idea what really makes the contraption run. We call the reaction 'combustion' because it nicely conceals our lack of knowledge on just what takes place in the engine cylinder. I just don't think we can live in this atmosphere of ignorance about what goes on there when our whole business depends upon it."

After having contributed air-cooling to Frigidaire, Kettering continued his interest and activity in domestic refrigeration and air conditioning. Among the many further contributions in which he had a part, by far the most important was the altogether new refrigerant, "Freon." When several years ago it became apparent that, if ever air conditioning was to have wide use, a better refrigerant was needed than the noxious sulfur dioxide or the poisonous methyl chloride, he interested Thomas Midgley, Jr., in undertaking a search for such a compound. Out of the intensive efforts that followed came the surprising fluorine-containing compounds which were named "Freon," and which are so completely non-toxic and so free from the fire hazard also that they are now used in practically all air conditioning and domestic refrigeration.

As head of the General Motors Research Laboratories, Kettering played a greater part than that of administrator in the front office. But among his administrative functions there was one to which he gave his serious attention. This was the choosing of proper research projects. It is his view that picking the problems to work on is the important element in industrial research. "Nearly every item in an encyclopedia is something that research might be done on," he said.

Once a research endeavor had been decided upon, he took an active part in what was done on it. He was everywhere, imparting enthusiasm to those engaged in the work and often taking part in the experimentation as well. "I think anything more than two feet away from the job you are working on is too far," he said.

In guiding the efforts of those associated with him, he suggested rather than directed. So great was his respect for independent thought and initiative in others that it was often difficult for those working on a project to find out just what he himself thought ought to be done in a given circumstance. He was careful not to stamp out a spark of fire in anyone. Instead, he would fan it to a bright glow. If he did any prodding of those working on an endeavor, it was done so subtly that they were likely not to recognize it as such. Mostly they were aware only of his intense interest.

But right in this area lay one of Kettering's principal shortcomings. Because of a distaste for administrative matters, he sometimes dodged the responsibilities of his position. He has said on various occasions that he never quite arrived at being an executive, that he had always refused to be tied down to an administrative job, and that he was the world's worst manager. Although those self-estimates were harsher than was warranted, it is true that he did not always step up to some administrative duties which were important and which should have been his.

Nevertheless, because of Kettering's versatility and eminent capabilities with people, there were some in General Motors who wanted him to be given a larger part in the administrative affairs of the corporation. But Alfred P. Sloan, Jr., as president of General Motors and one who was close enough to Kettering to understand him well, protected him from any move of that kind. "Doing so would have been to water down one of the most valuable assets the corporation has," Sloan said. "He is so tremendously engrossed in his research endeavors and he is making such outstanding contributions through them that it would be a mistake to divert his attention to something else."

In 1953 Sloan testified also that some years earlier when

n his office as head of the General Motors Research Corporation, 1924.

First home of the General Motors Research Corporation, now the Research Staff. Here in 1920 Kettering began his productive career as head of research for General Motors.

In this Dayton, Ohio, filling station in February, 1923, gasoline containing the newly discovered antiknock agent, tetraethyl lead, first began to be sold. It was named "Ethyl Gasoline" but was called "Ethyl Gas" for short.

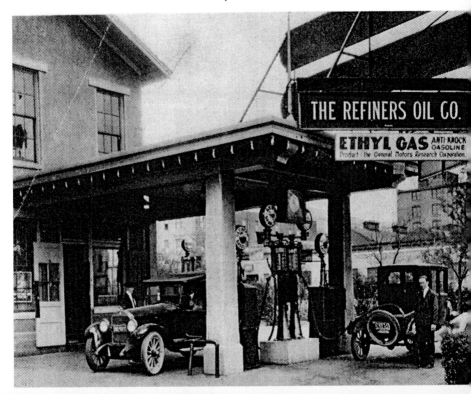

it had been proposed to make Kettering a member of the important Policy Committee of General Motors, the suggestion was rejected for another reason. This was concern on the part of members of the committee that they would be so carried away by all his fascinating talk about the wonders of tomorrow that they would not have time to attend to the necessary business of today.

Sloan recognized that Kettering's influence in the success of General Motors went far beyond the contributions he was making through science and engineering. Just a few years before Kettering retired as head of research for General Motors, which he did in 1947, Sloan gave an evaluation of the part he had been playing in its success. "I start with the very ordinary statement that Mr. Kettering's contribution to General Motors has been most outstanding," said Sloan. "And I would say that that contribution divides itself into the tangibles and the intangibles. On the tangible side are the things that are specific. . . . However, I am not dealing with that. . . . I would say that the intangible side of it, if it could be evaluated, has meant more to all of us than all the tangible things, important as they are.

"He has been an inspiration to me and to the whole organization, particularly in directing our thoughts and our imagination and our activities toward doing a better job technically and the tremendous importance of technological progress. . . . Also, his courage, his tenacity, his belief in the soundness of his deductions and his work have been essential, because nobody knows better than you the terrible resistance you get in trying to do something different."

Kettering expressed his feelings in a message sent to Sloan at Christmastime in 1943: "I just want to drop you a note and tell you how much I appreciate being a part of the great General Motors organization, which has grown in importance and influence in the years under your wise management."

XV

"IDEAS GROW VERY MUCH like plants," said Kettering. "You have to sow the seed. Then, when the shoots first come through the ground, they are quite tender and vulnerable. The proper care of the plant in this state is very important, if it is to live and grow.

"In doing a new thing, only occasionally does anything go right. At least ninety per cent of the time is taken up in overcoming all sorts of new and unexpected difficulties.

"It has been my good fortune to go through at least a dozen of these new developments. And the life histories of all of them are very much the same. In each there is a period which I have called the shirt-losing zone. That is the time, after the article has been put on the market, when it gets a serious setback. This is the most dangerous period, and many good ideas must have failed at this point."

The story of tetraethyl lead and "Ethyl" gasoline as a cure for knock in the automobile engine, one of Kettering's early and major developments, is, he often said, a typical instance of the tough and toilsome process by which new and improved products have to be brought into being. It is the story of tetraethyl lead, with all that came out of it, that is told in this chapter.

The incentive for Kettering's long effort to overcome the noisy bugbear of knock was the desire to conserve gasoline by making it possible to boost the compression of automobile engines and so to get more miles per gallon. Knock sets a barrier to such a boost, he would explain, for it gets worse and worse as pressure is raised, until at last it becomes destructive in its violence. But high compression is the key to getting the most out of gasoline. That is so because the tighter the charge is squeezed on the upstroke of the piston before ignition the further the hot gases can expand on the downstroke after combustion, or the stronger and the more sustained the push they can give.

Some of the early events in the effort to find a cure for knock in the gasoline engine have already been recounted (in Chapter XII). It has been related that in 1916, after the bugbear of knock had twice bobbed up as an obstacle in Kettering's path, he had interested Thomas Midgley, Jr., in joining him in an effort to learn just what knock is and to search for some way to eliminate it. Soon in their thinking they speculated that dyeing a fuel red might make it knock less. Although that theory quickly proved to be wrong, the chance selection of iodine to color the fuel red led to an important discovery, the discovery that knock *is* suppressed by putting a pinch of iodine into the fuel.

It was shortly before United States entry into World War I that the effectiveness of iodine as a suppressor of knock was found. But, as has already been explained, iodine is not a substance that can be used practically for this purpose. Just as soon as the war was over, therefore, Kettering and his associates renewed the effort to find a practical cure for knock in the automobile engine.

The search had been pursued only a short while more when it was discovered that nitrogen, too, in organic nitrogen compounds such as aniline, is an effective suppressor of knock in engines. The aniline-type compounds seemed so nearly practical as antiknock agents that for many months most of the effort was spent in searching for a way to use them commercially.

When the General Motors Research Corporation was formed, the effort to eliminate knock thus became one of the principal projects pursued there. And in an early experiment on boosted compression the compression ratio of an automobile engine—a Chevrolet it was—was raised from the then normal value of 4 to 1 up to 7 to 1, thus almost doubling it. That car of higher compression had superior performance. Because it therefore had unusual hill-climbing ability for that time and also because the engine exhaust smelled so badly from the nitrogen compound used as antiknock agent, it was dubbed "The Goat." Nevertheless, it gave an increase of 40 per cent or more in miles per gallon over the corresponding car of conventional compression.

But, as often happens, the research arrived before long at one of its lowest points. The difficulties with the aniline compounds, one of which was their disagreeable odor, had gradually made it apparent that the chances of utilizing them successfully were not bright. Although many other compounds had been tested meanwhile, nothing else effective that appeared practical had been found. At that time Midgley was so disheartened that he asked Kettering for permission to give up the quest for an antiknock agent.

It so happened that Kettering was leaving just then on a trip to New York. He said, "I will talk to you when I get back." Returning on the train from New York with the fuel problem still very much on his mind, his eye happened to fall on a newspaper item headed, "University Professor Discovers Universal Solvent."

Because he knew a humorous story about two chemists who persuaded a banker to back them in an effort to find a "universal solvent," that item attracted his attention. The story was that, while the two men were working away in their effort to make the universal solvent, some skeptic asked them, "When you fellows get that stuff that will dissolve everything in the world, just what are you going to keep it in?"

Because Kettering knew that story, he clipped out the item which told about a compound of selenium, and the next day he gave it to those working on the endeavor with the suggestion that they try that compound as a possible suppressor of knock. This was one of the events that led to the discovery that compounds of selenium have an anti-knock effect five times as great as anything discovered before. And that in turn led to the discovery that compounds of the similar element, tellurium, are four times as powerful as selenium, or twenty times as effective as anything known before. These new and exciting discoveries naturally lifted the endeavor out of the swamp of discouragement.

But the trouble was that tellurium compounds smelled like a devilish mixture of garlic and onions. The foul odor got into the men's systems and on their clothes. They couldn't wash it off, for water only made the odor worse. The smell was so bad that anyone working with tellurium was virtually a social outcast. For this and other reasons any thought of using tellurium had to be abandoned.

The search for a practical antiknock agent was, therefore, taken up again. With the knowledge gained up to that time, this further search was conducted in a more systematic fashion, which Midgley called "a scientific fox hunt." That hunt led at last to tetraethyl lead. This truly remarkable compound is a liquid which looks like gasoline, does not smell bad, and is far more effective in suppressing knock than even the foul-smelling tellurium.

The effort to see whether tetraethyl lead would be an antiknock agent came as a projection from prior results obtained in that systematic program. As no such compound was in existence, it had to be made in the laboratory. And this proved difficult. At last, after some mysterious and disheartening failures, a minute amount of the compound was obtained, and the great moment arrived when it was to be tested in the engine for antiknock effect.

With the men who were working on the endeavor gathered around the little engine, it was run on fuel containing a very small amount of the tetraethyl lead added purely by guess. And the engine purred along completely free of knock. An equal amount of untreated fuel was then poured in, cutting the concentration of the new compound in half. Still there was no sign of knock. This same process of halving the concentration of tetraethyl lead was repeated again and again and again, while the excitement of the observers mounted higher and higher with each dilution. In the end it was found that as an antiknock agent tetraethyl lead was fifty times as effective as the aniline on which so much work had been done earlier. This astonishing determination was made on December 9, 1921, a day which in its exciting events was for Kettering, as he said afterward, the most dramatic in his whole research career.

Not long after that great day, however, came a distressing discovery. It was found that gasoline containing tetraethyl lead left solid deposits in the engine, deposits which resulted in serious spark plug erosion and exhaust valve burning.

That trouble was not accepted as an insurmountable obstacle, however. Instead, extensive search was begun at once for a means of overcoming the difficulty. The investigation extended over many months and involved during much of that time the running of a dozen engines twenty-four hours a day. Thousands of miles were run in various types of automobile tests, too. All this led to the fortunate discovery that the troubles could be corrected by adding to the gasoline along with tetraethyl lead an organic compound of bromine, or of bromine and chlorine.

Just after the marvelous effectiveness of tetraethyl lead for stopping knock had been discovered and before these corrective agents had been found, small samples were given to various persons to try. One of those persons was F. E. Moskovics, president of the company making the Marmon automobile. Moskovics was so enthusiastic about the effects of the stuff in his car that he asked if he could not have some more. It was suggested that he might like to wait for a further supply until some way could be found to solve the valve deposit and spark plug troubles. But right back from Moskovics came a letter, saying, "Bad as it is, I should like to have some more."

In the early part of 1923 it was decided to begin selling to the public in an experimental way gasoline treated with tetraethyl lead. That was before all the research on an agent to correct the spark plug and valve-burning problems had been completed. But corrective agents that were reasonably good had by then been found.

"You may ask," said Kettering, "why we did not wait to begin selling the product until all the problems of using it had been completely solved. The answer is this: I have found that once a product has reached the stage at which it is useful to people, or better than what they have otherwise, it is time to begin making it available to them. Doing this serves two purposes. The first is that people get the benefit of the improvement sooner than they would otherwise. And the second is that the further improvement of the product will proceed faster and more intelligently when there is such practical use to stimulate it and guide it."

Thinking that a trade name for the product simpler than the chemical name, tetraethyl lead, was needed, Kettering suggested the name "Ethyl" gasoline. Also, to give the gasoline a distinctive appearance, it was decided to dye it red.

There was in Dayton a small but thriving gasoline marketing organization, the Refiners Oil Company. Kettering knew

W. E. Talbot, the manager of that company, and induced him to become the first distributor of the new product. Thus it was that at the beginning of February, 1923, the sale of "Ethyl" gasoline was begun in an experimental way at a single station of the Refiners Oil Company on South Main Street in Dayton, Ohio.

"The reaction from the public as they began to use this new material was very encouraging," Kettering recalled, "and in the spring of 1923 we organized the General Motors Chemical Company to take charge of its distribution. I was president of this new company and Midgley was vice-president and general manager."

As the sales of "Ethyl" gasoline in that one station of the Refiners Oil Company increased, a second station was added. And soon the sale was begun in Cincinnati by the same company. It was then that there was undertaken for the first time a program of advertising the product in Dayton and Cincinnati newspapers. It was at this time, too, that the "Ethyl" emblem—a circle enclosing a black triangle bearing the word "Ethyl" in yellow and with yellow lines radiating from it like sunbeams—which has since appeared on so many, many pumps and in other places, was designed by Henry T. Ewald of the Campbell-Ewald advertising agency.

In the meantime Kettering and Midgley were trying to interest some of the major oil companies in improving the antiknock quality of their gasoline by adding tetraethyl lead. For the most part they met with skepticism and opposition. The president of one of the oil companies they visited was particularly antagonistic. "Do you question the integrity of our company?" he said hotly. "Our gasoline is the best in the world. I ought to throw you men out of this fourteenth-story window."

But, fortunately, in the summer of 1923 they were able to persuade the officials of the Standard Oil Company (Indiana) to become the first major oil company to sell "Ethyl" gasoline. A factor of importance in helping to bring this about was the presence of Robert E. Wilson on the research staff of the Standard Oil Company. Shortly before that time Wilson had gone to the Standard Oil Company from the faculty of Massachusetts Institute of Technology. At MIT he had been director of the Research Laboratory of Applied Chemistry and in charge of a research project on tetraethyl lead instituted there by the General Motors Research Corporation as a supplement to its own program of experimentation. Another favorable factor was that the president of the Standard Old Company then was Dr. William M. Burton, a man who had himself been a distinguished chemist. This action of the Standard Old Company in undertaking the sale of "Ethyl" gasoline in all its many stations was important in helping to bring about the acceptance of the new product elsewhere.

All this time the little concern was hard pressed by another grave problem—where to get the bromine needed. It was early foreseen that, if "Ethyl" gasoline was to be sold in the huge quantities hoped for, there would not be enough bromine to serve as the corrective agent. What little bromine had been needed before the coming of "Ethyl" gasoline was readily obtained as a by-product in treating the brine from Michigan salt wells. But this new demand was expected to become so huge that it could not be met with bromine from salt wells.

A survey of other possible sources of bromine was accordingly conducted, during which Kettering made a trip to Zarzis in Tunisia, North Africa, to inspect the bromine-containing waters there, which the French had developed as a source of supply for making tear gas in World War I. However, it was concluded that the source of bromine should be domestic if possible.

149

Unfortunately, there is practically no bromine in our Great Salt Lake, but it was known that bromine is present in the sea. It occurs there, however, in very, very minute concentration—only sixty-five parts per million. That means that it takes about ten tons of sea water to contain one pound of bromine.

When Kettering consulted the suppliers of bromine about the likelihood of getting bromine out of the sea, they replied that in their opinion it would not be at all possible. "Why," they said, "there is far more bromine left in our brine after we get through processing it for the extraction of bromine than there is in sea water in the first place!"

But with his usual unwillingness to believe that anything is impossible, Kettering decided that an intensive effort should be made anyway to see if a process for getting bromine out of sea water could not be found. All the research men concerned with the "Ethyl" endeavor joined forces and set out vigorously in search of a process for getting bromine out of the sea. And after a great deal of intensive effort a way was found.

This came about because Kettering would not take no for an answer. "You have to try things," he says. "Action without intelligence is a form of insanity, but intelligence without action is the greatest form of stupidity in the world."

In August, 1924, the General Motors Chemical Company was superseded by Ethyl Gasoline Corporation (now Ethyl Corporation). That company was formed jointly by General Motors Corporation and the Standard Oil Company of New Jersey. The joint company formed in this way was thought to be the best means of making "Ethyl" gasoline available throughout the oil industry. Kettering continued for a while as president of the new company, Frank A. Howard of the

Standard Oil Company was vice-president, and Midgley was general manager.

Among the many problems that arose in the application of tetraethyl lead there was another major one of serious concern. From the outset in the development of the "Ethyl" idea it was appreciated that putting tetraethyl lead into gasoline might possibly introduce a health hazard. The first opinions of the doctors who were consulted were full of such frightening phrases as "grave fears," "distinct risk," "widespread lead poisoning," and the like. But, fortunately, after long and thorough investigation it was found that, when its distribution and use are controlled by proper safeguards, there is no hazard to health from gasoline containing tetraethyl lead.

These investigations, which covered many months, were made chiefly by the U.S. Public Health Service, the U.S. Bureau of Mines, and Ethyl Corporation. Surgeon General Hugh S. Cumming was head of the U.S. Public Health Service then. He appointed a committee of recognized authorities in medicine, physiology, and industrial hygiene to conduct a thorough investigation of any possible hazards to the health of those using or selling gasoline containing tetraethyl lead. The months of intensive study that followed were conducted for the committee under the direction of Dr. J. P. Leake, surgeon of the U.S. Public Health Service.

The tests conducted by Ethyl Corporation itself were under the guidance of Dr. Robert A. Kehoe, professor of physiology, College of Medicine, University of Cincinnati, who later became medical director of Ethyl Corporation. At the U.S. Bureau of Mines the investigation was made at the Pittsburgh Station of which Dr. A. C. Fieldner was then director. Fieldner put W. P. Yant in direct charge of the tests, in which animals in a large chamber were exposed for several hours each day to the diluted exhaust from an engine running on gasoline containing tetraethyl lead. After some months of such experiments, no indication of lead poisoning was found in any of the animals exposed.

During the period of that exposure five puppies were actually born in the chamber, and they spent each day there during the remaining period of the tests, all without harm of any kind. The men working on the job christened those puppies "The 'Ethyl' Gas Hounds."

For about a year during the period of investigation, because of apprehension in some quarters, Ethyl Corporation discontinued the sale of "Ethyl" gasoline until the U.S. Public Health Service could complete its tests and make its report. When that report—with its favorable outcome—was issued, the sale of "Ethyl" gasoline was resumed. The companies which before had been distributors gladly put up the sign, "Ethyl Is Back," and their customers welcomed it.

But for Ethyl Corporation the period just passed in the life history of the new product was definitely that which Kettering calls "the shirt-losing zone." For, although now the number of companies distributing the product and the amount of it sold increased at a rapid rate, the red figures on the books of the company mounted to a total of over three million dollars before the color changed to black.

Speaking about his experiences in the "Ethyl" endeavor, Kettering said: "In putting out new things troubles are not the exception. They are the rule. That is why I have said on so many occasions that the price of progress is trouble."

Some of these same difficulties were experienced when it came time to introduce "Ethyl" gasoline into England and other countries. In England a Departmental Committee on Ethyl Petrol, authorized by Parliament and appointed by the Minister of Health, made another investigation of possible hazards to the health of the people. Fortunately, that committee reported: "The results of our experiments agree with the results of the experiments carried out in the United States of America."

Among the prominent Englishmen whom Kettering met at this time was Sir Josiah Stamp, later Lord Stamp and chief economist of the Bank of England. Sir Josiah was negative to the introduction of "Ethyl" gasoline into England. His arguments were based in part upon the idea that it is not possible to have a stable economic world if it is going to be upset continually by the introduction of new inventions.

In 1938 Kettering had a further experience with Lord Stamp, which he afterward related as follows: "I had just returned to England from Germany; and, knowing that over there they were getting ready to go to war, I asked Lord Stamp whether or not England felt prepared to meet it. He replied that it was not necessary that England be prepared for war, because Germany could not fight a long war. In support of his view, he pulled out a piece of paper and set up the relative percentages of Germany's gold reserves and various other indexes which are commonly used in rating a nation's commercial ability or industrial activity. He said that, with Germany's indexes so low, she would go broke before she could even start an important war.

"This opinion of his proved to be a great fallacy, of course. And it was unfortunate that Lord Stamp and his Lady were killed by a German bomb which fell at their home outside London. I should like to have been able to discuss this subject with him further. But I'm not sure," added Kettering in his humorous way, "whether economists and inventors will get to the same place when they die."

Because Ethyl Corporation needed a full-time president, Kettering withdrew as head of it early in 1925. He was succeeded by Earle W. Webb, who served as president for more than twenty years, and was succeeded in turn by Edward L. Shea and more recently by B. Bynum Turner. But Kettering remained on the board of directors of the company and has continued to give it his active interest and assistance.

After the question of possible hazard to health had been settled so positively, the product went forward rapidly in this country and was soon introduced into other countries as well. Then, in 1933, tetraethyl lead began to be put into regular-priced gasolines. Within a few years nearly all automobile gasoline sold contained tetraethyl lead as a knock suppressor.

Tetraethyl lead was put into aviation gasoline, too, thereby boosting its octane number. And the availability of it made it possible for the U.S. Army Air Corps in 1937 to make 100-octane aviation gasoline the standard fuel for combat planes. This greatly improved airplane fuel was thus ready in time to play the vital part it did in helping to win World War II. "I think we wouldn't have won the Battle of Britain without 100-octane," said Great Britain's wartime petroleum secretary.

Although tetraethyl lead is a powerful suppressor of knock, the degree of its effectiveness is limited and the magnitude of it depends also upon the composition of the gasoline to which it is added. For that reason Kettering and his research associates next took up an effort to find what kinds of hydrocarbons are most free from knock on their own account—what is the best composition for gasoline itself to have. Kettering said he did not believe that Nature could have had the automobile in mind when she made petroleum, any more than the hog intended his bristles for toothbrushes. So he wanted to find out just what kinds of hydrocarbons are best in gasoline, and then if possible to discover ways of converting natural products into such materials. "We don't expect to get finished crankshafts out of an iron mine," he would say. "Then why should we expect to find in crude oil as it comes out of the ground oil molecules of the particular form that is best for gasoline?"

The men most active in this further investigation were, first, Graham Edgar, research director of Ethyl Corporation, who made some of the early discoveries; then Wheeler G. Lovell and John M. Campbell of the General Motors Research Laboratories, who carried the investigation forward and established the basic rules relating hydrocarbon composition, or structure, to freedom from knock. Later the pioneering observations of these men were verified and extended by other investigators. What all these men found out, in a word, was that the gasoline engine does not like fuels containing long, skinny hydrocarbon molecules but that it does like fuels made up of short, plump hydrocarbon pieces.

Soon, with this knowledge before them, petroleum refiners began to develop and introduce into petroleum refining new processes—processes which did more than merely separate from crude oil what was in it naturally. Thus refining techniques which changed the composition of petroleum hydrocarbons into more nearly knock-free forms gradually came into use. And, with the supplementary aid of tetraethyl lead as an antiknock agent, these brought large improvements in gasoline.

This did not come about, however, without a great deal of selling effort, an effort in which Kettering had a principal part. A disbelief in the benefits of such changes, and even prejudice against them, was for a long time almost universal. This was true of both engineers and executives in the automobile industry and of those in the oil industry.

Kettering considers those two industries natural partners in serving the public. And to the men in the oil industry he was a constant missionary on behalf of more knock-free gasolines—that is, higher octane gasolines which would make it possible to boost the compression of automobile engines. But almost everyone in the oil industry thought that making gasolines much higher in octane number was simply not practical. The cost would be so high and the loss in volume yield so great that no net gain to the user would result. A typical opinion, as expressed in 1946 by a prominent research man in the industry, was that the upper limit of octane number had by then become pretty well stabilized and probably would not change much.

But Kettering kept saying that you can't stop the rise in octane number until nature stops it for you. And, from the extensive researches on automobile fuels being pursued by his own men and others, he knew that the end of nature's string in that respect was far from having been reached. "Here is one of the greatest steps in the world," he said, "wide open like a prairie." It remained only to find how to make such fuels in a practical way.

Now, thanks to the marvelous new refining processes resulting from brilliant and persistent research by the petroleum people, his prediction is fast coming true. Meanwhile, over the years, men of the oil industry have come to think so highly of Kettering's zealous efforts toward such improvement that in 1948 the American Petroleum Institute chose him as the recipient of its highest award, the API Gold Medal for Distinguished Achievement. One prominent executive of the oil industry generously said that Kettering's work had benefited them so greatly that, in all fairness, the oil industry, not the automobile industry, ought to have been paying his salary.

Some automobile engineers meanwhile were saying that they would like to see the compression of automobile engines lowered, not raised. And most engineers in the industry thought that any further increases in automobile engine compression were not practical. Such engines, they said, would be altogether too rough and harsh in operation to be tolerated by automobile drivers. They would have very high piston friction, and therefore low mechanical efficiency. High compression would introduce insurmountable ignition prob- lems, too, and it would not improve fuel economy very much, if any.

But Kettering's response was that "to get high engine effi- ciencies, explosion pressures have to be high. There is no other way. . . . If you can get high economy with low ex- plosion pressures, write me a letter about it. I would like to know how it is done."

So, with all the knowledge gained up to that time, Ketter- ing set out immediately after World War II to build a sam- ple automobile engine of very high compression. It was his philosophy that to sell anything you have to have a sample. "I have no patience," he said, "with the fellow who says, 'I have been telling them for years and they don't pay any at- tention to me.' All he has done is to talk to them."

After preliminary experiments with a single-cylinder en- gine having compression ratios up to 15 to 1, an automo- bile engine having a compression ratio of 12.5 to 1, twice as high as the average at that time, was built and put into a car. That high-compression engine, built with knowledge gained through all the years of research, proved not to have in serious form any of the difficulties the critics had pre- dicted. Also in the highly important item of miles per gal- lon it gave a gain of 35 to 45 per cent.

Kettering now prepared the second of his historic papers on "More Efficient Utilization of Fuel," a companion to one he had presented in 1919, early in his long campaign. In this second paper he gave a history of the effort to get knock-free fuels and the high-compression engines to utilize them, and he presented the results just obtained with a car of really high compression when run on gasoline free from knock.

Before the Society of Automotive Engineers he presented that paper, so significant in pointing the way upward in fuels and engines. This was in June, 1947, just after the announcement of his retirement as head of research for General Motors. He was then past the normal age for retirement, because he had wanted to stay on long enough to bring to such a definite stage of advancement his long fight to break down the barriers to high compression and better fuel economy.

Even that was not the end of the campaign, but only one stage of progress in it. He was, therefore, happy to be succeeded as head of research for General Motors by Charles L. McCuen. McCuen, a General Motors engineer of long experience both as an engineer and as an administrator—he had been chief engineer and later general manager at Oldsmobile—Kettering knew to be admirably fitted to carry forward the work on fuels and high compression.

On the day of Kettering's retirement in 1947 he said this: "The forward-looking work on fuels and engines could not be in better shape than it is now. . . . Engineers everywhere are thinking now in the right direction." In expression of his characteristic patience, he said, too: "I don't care just how long it takes to gain the full advantage of high compression. Any rate of progress toward it is all right, just so long as we are headed in the right direction."

But already, as a result of the progress in which Kettering was a principal pioneer, two gallons of gasoline are doing the work three used to do. Since the people of this nation are now spending fourteen billion dollars a year for gasoline, the savings these advances have brought amount to about five billion dollars a year. And this is not to mention the billions of gallons of gasoline conserved for future use.

XVI

J. BROOK JACKSON WENT into Kettering's office one morning in the late 1920's and found him with blueprints spread over his desk. In answer to the question on Jackson's face, Kettering said: "After a fellow gets to a certain age, Brook, he does one of two things. Either he buys a yacht or he gets a new wife. I think I'll buy a yacht."

But the reason Kettering wanted a yacht was not the usual one. It was because of his long interest in the diesel engine, which usually powered such boats. Although the diesel engine—an engine in which ignition is by heat of compression instead of by an electric spark—had been invented by Rudolf Diesel in the 1890's, not many such engines were in use in the late twenties. This was true especially in Kettering's field of transportation. There were a few diesel engines on boats and some were used in stationary power service. But he wanted to find out just why they were not employed in other places, such as on the railroad.

It was to help him learn about this that Kettering purchased a yacht from the Defoe Shipbuilding Company, Bay City, Michigan. He christened it the *Olive K* for Mrs. Kettering. But he called it his floating laboratory, and with it he ran quickly into one of the principal difficulties with the diesel engine at that time. The means of injecting fuel into the cylinders was so imperfect, he found, that the engine had to be nursed constantly. He almost wore out the iron stairs to the engine room, he said, tramping up and down them so often to see how smoky the exhaust was after he had tried to make some improvement in the injection system. In a letter to Carl G. Fisher, he wrote: "At the present time my opinion of the diesel engine is not fit to put in print."

Whenever, with the alertness Kettering had for such things, he sensed anything out of the ordinary in the engine room he would go directly there to see what he might do or learn. Once when he had as guests on the *Olive K* some of his associates of the research staff, and while the steward was serving the soup course in the dining room, he became aware that the engine was not running right. So he left the table and went to the engine room. He was gone nearly an hour, while the men and the dinner waited. Then he returned, all smiles because he had found how to correct some difficulty.

Because of Kettering's disappointing experience with that first boat, which was not built to his specifications, he soon commissioned the Defoe Shipbuilding Company to construct for him as a replacement a second boat, one after his own ideas. This one was larger, 170 feet in length, with a beam of 26 feet. He wanted it big enough for taking ocean cruises, and he was advised that that was about the minimum size for such service. This yacht was designed by the New York firm of Cox and Stevens, in conjunction with John H. Wells, Inc., naval architects. But Kettering made it plain, Harry Defoe recalled, that what he wanted most of all was an engine room with diesel engines in it.

He also wanted this boat to be free from all the major shortcomings he had experienced in his first yacht and observed in others. In a letter to Carl Fisher he gave some of his ideas at the time: "I am figuring . . . now on having a boat built, about 165 to 170 feet long, more or less as an experiment, to see if it is possible to build a diesel boat that will not have a lot of noise and vibration about it. Certainly, I have never seen one yet but what was full of vibration. . . . I would like to build a boat so you would think you were being towed." To one who had put so much effort into smoothing the running of automobile engines that quaking in boats was distressing indeed.

How to build a boat free from vibration was something to which he devoted his best ingenuity. As he wrote further to Carl Fisher, "It is my impression that any two-engine boat has got to have some method of synchronizing the two engines." He therefore came up with a scheme by which the power pulses in the two engines could be held in step, thus making them run in such perfect unison that, as was said by Captain Val J. Shaughnessy, master of the second *Olive K,* "there was not a ripple on the boat."

A number of other advanced features were incorporated in the second *Olive K,* some of which also came out of Kettering's imagination and ingenuity. One of these was an automatic radio and phonograph of his design, operated in connection with the telephone system. The yacht had the best in automatic steering apparatus available. It had a radio direction finder, a Fathometer, and other equipment. It was fitted also with a mechanical stabilizer, a device to prevent roll and to hold the boat steady in rough seas.

When the first trial trip of the second *Olive K* was made, there was a large party aboard. It had been planned that the owner should conduct the guests on an inspection tour of the yacht and be host at dinner. But he was down in the engine room, where his principal interest lay. When Harry Defoe urged him to come up and take the traditional part of the owner of the fine new yacht, he said he wished he could hire a person to play the part of owner. What with smudge from the engine on his hands and clothes, he did not quite look like the owner of such a fine yacht.

The experience with diesel engines that Kettering was thus getting on his yacht was meanwhile being supplemented in an extensive way with experimentation he instigated in the Research Laboratories. That work, headed first by G. E. A. Hallett and later by F. G. Shoemaker, showed that there were three principal shortcomings of the diesel engine which kept it from being more useful in the field of transportation. Besides the difficulty of bad fuel injection already mentioned, the diesel engines of that time were much too big and heavy, and pistons and rings had to be serviced and replaced altogether too often.

One by one, through painstaking experimentation in the Research Laboratories, those three major difficulties were overcome. To make the diesel lighter, the decision of Kettering and his associates was that it should be a two-cycle engine, one that gives a power pulse at every downstroke of the piston. "The weight of the diesel engine was in somebody's head," Kettering said. "Diesel engines do not have to be heavy. We always want to blame our ignorance on the engine. It is like the doctors with their incurable diseases. Did you ever stop to think what an incurable disease is? It is one the doctor doesn't know how to cure."

For that old diesel problem of how to keep pistons and rings from requiring too-frequent attention the solution found was to cool the piston head from underneath with a jet of oil, and to insert a thin section called a "heat dam" between the piston head and the ring belt. That heat dam kept the high heat of combustion from running down to the rings and coking the coil in which they ran, and so causing the rings to stick tight in their grooves. This is merely the same principle as is used in a metal-handled teapot to keep the handle from getting too hot to hold, but it increased piston life tenfold.

That improved piston came out of a long series of engine experiments designed to ask the diesel engine itself just what it would like most in the way of a piston. It was of this work that Kettering said: "Quit butting in with your theories and let the engine do the talking. You are a good engineer, to be sure; but were you ever a piston in a diesel engine?"

"You can't 'edict' material," he said, too. "That is one thing the engineer ought to learn early. He is only an errand boy for ideas."

The direct method of "asking the engine itself" Kettering called experimental evaluation. He recognized that some investigators look down on that procedure and call it the cut-and-try or the trial-and-error method. But why don't the critics talk instead about the "trial-and-*success*" method? he queried. That is what it really is.

Some of the efforts to improve the operation of the diesel engine were made at what was originally the Winton Engine Company in Cleveland but is now the Cleveland Diesel Engine Division of General Motors. The Winton Engine Company became a part of General Motors in 1930, following an understanding between Kettering and Alfred P. Sloan, Jr., president of General Motors. "I was to buy the best available business then making diesels," said Sloan, "so that we could most quickly achieve contact with the practical side of current practice, and Ket was to determine how the engine ought to be made." George W. Codrington was general manager of Winton and Carl Salisbury was chief engineer.

This question of what was the most practical way to get a good diesel engine was for Kettering more than a simple development endeavor. Some topside men in General Motors kept advocating that the corporation get into the diesel engine business not by the development route which he was pursuing but by purchasing rights and know-how from one of the old-established European companies making diesel engines.

But Kettering made a determined resistance to that proposal. This he did because, from his experience and his visits to the plants of diesel engine makers in Europe, he thought that none of those engines, nor the understanding of the men who made them, was good enough to meet the requirements as he saw them. "If you are going into new work, I can tell you," said he out of his experience in this and other fields, "that the biggest job you will have is to strong-arm the opposition of well-meaning people."

One of the most persistent advocates of obtaining the rights to make one of those European diesels was an executive of what is now the GMC Truck and Coach Division. To him Kettering said more than once, "If I felt as you do I would buy a half dozen of those European diesel engines, put them in buses and see how they work out." At last his company did just that.

But in bus service those engines did not turn out at all well. They caused so much trouble, in fact, that the exasperated executive told Kettering he would like to take him out and tar and feather him for his advice to get those awful diesel engines.

"But I didn't advise you to get them at all," Kettering replied. "What I said was that, *if I felt as you did,* I would buy some of them to try. I thought that was the only way to cure you of your insistence that we take on the making of one of those European diesels."

After many months of experimentation and development in the Research Laboratories, mostly on one-cylinder diesel engines, it was decided to build some multicylinder engines of the new type based on the best of what had been learned up to that time. Furthermore, it was planned to install those engines in the General Motors Building, just then being constructed as a part of the Century of Progress Exposition held in Chicago in 1933. There the engines were to run electric generators and furnish part of the light and power for the building and the exhibits. They were not to be hidden away but were themselves to be a conspicuous part of the exhibit. Two such engines of 600-horsepower each were accordingly constructed at the Winton Division. They were only one-fifth the weight and one-fourth the size of other diesels of comparable power at that time.

Those two diesel engines running at the Century of Progress Exposition were seen by Ralph Budd, president of the Burlington Lines, who wanted a small streamline train to try to regain some of the passenger traffic lost to buses and airplanes. At Budd's request a third one of those engines was built to power the little train he wanted. The cars were to be furnished by the Edward G. Budd Company of Philadelphia and to be covered with stainless steel.

That 600-horsepower diesel engine, together with suitable electric generators and motors to transmit its power to the axles, was installed in the lead car of the little streamline train by the Electro-Motive Division of General Motors. Electro-Motive was a small concern in Cleveland which for some years had been building gasoline-powered rail cars and which became a part of General Motors shortly after the acquisition of Winton. H. L. Hamilton was president of the Electro-Motive Division and Richard M. Dilworth, chief engineer.

That first train powered by the new diesel engine was completed in 1934 and named the *Pioneer Zephyr*. It was such a novelty, and the interest of the public in it was so great, that the Burlington people sent it around the country on an exhibition tour during which it was viewed by millions of people.

In the experiments Kettering was conducting meanwhile on the *Olive K* he took several cruises. These consisted of a number on the Great Lakes during his summer holidays, mostly to Georgian Bay; a cruise to the Galápagos Islands in

1930; one to ports of Cuba and other islands of the West Indies in 1931; one to Yucatán and the Mayan ruins in 1932; and one to Veracruz and Mexico City in 1933. The last four were wintertime cruises made from Miami, Florida, as port of departure, and in them Kettering combined other interests with diesel experimentation.

On each cruise Kettering invited a number of friends to accompany him. In inviting his guests, his aim was to get some congenial fellows who, as he said, would let him alone. He was quite serious about wanting guests who could entertain themselves for the most part, because he wanted them to have a good time and he wished also to be free to spend a great portion of his own time in the engine room.

As one of his guests said, "Ket makes you feel that the yacht belongs to you, and not to him." Nevertheless, he contributed immensely to the interest of life on the *Olive K.* Julius Stone, guest on a number of the cruises, said he would give a fortune if he could have a recording of the never-to-be-forgotten conversations at dinner and in the evening when the men were together. It was Kettering with his marvelous stories and wise and humorous sayings who formed the center of that interest.

On a certain summer day while the *Olive K* was in Georgian Bay, one of the extraordinary events of Kettering's lifetime occurred. The men on the yacht went out fishing early one morning. They intended to catch some fish and cook them for breakfast on an island nearby. Not caring to fish himself, Kettering went to the island while his guests fished. He set about building a fire and making preparations for the breakfast. In doing so he exerted himself so much that he got very hot and perspired profusely. Later, when a cool breeze blew up, he was chilled.

Now, he had long been an inveterate cigar smoker, one who had a cigar in his mouth most of the time. But when after breakfast that morning he lit a cigar, it did not taste right, he said. He lit another, and then another, but none of them tasted good. And, although Mrs. Kettering kept his customary box of Perfecto cigars on hand for some time afterward, he never smoked another. Telling about the event afterward, Kettering said, "I didn't quit smoking. It just walked out from under me."

On the cruises of the second *Olive K* the injectors on the two diesel engines were of an entirely new type, a key development of the endeavor. Called the unit injector, this development ultimately put precision into fuel injection and solved completely the problem of unstable engine operation. But, sound as is the principle of those high-pressure injectors, the early mechanical application was so imperfect in some respects that, during the development period, the injectors did not always perform as intended. Once in a rough sea the engines were completely out of operation for twenty-four hours at a stretch. With the yacht rolling helplessly and most of the guests seasick, Kettering spent all that time in the engine room trying to correct the trouble. John L. Pratt, a vice-president of General Motors who was a guest on that cruise, remembers with admiration Kettering's persistence and dogged determination to make those injectors perform. He worked hour after hour under the most distressing circumstances, until at last he did overcome the difficulty. But the experience of drifting while Kettering tinkered came so often on such cruises, said Captain Shaughnessy, that ordinarily no one paid any attention.

The cruise across the Caribbean and through the Panama Canal to the Galápagos Islands in January and February, 1930, was the first major one of the second *Olive K*. As guests on that cruise Kettering had Dr. Roy D. McClure, surgeon-in-chief of the Henry Ford Hospital; Gar Wood, Detroit manufacturer and winner of Harmsworth Trophy races; John L. Pratt, a vice-president of General Motors; Julius F. Stone, Columbus manufacturer and Ohio State trustee; W. A. Chryst, chief engineer of Delco; Robert Lanphier, an executive of the Sangamo Electric Company; and Gene Kettering.

As recalled by Dr. McClure, the trip to the Galápagos was a wonderful seven weeks. In an account of the voyage Dr. McClure wrote this:

> So unique a host was Kettering that I constantly felt like calling him Captain Nemo, for *Twenty Thousand Leagues Under the Sea* was in my youth a favorite. Captain Nemo is not in the same class as Kettering. The synchronization of the twin diesel engines was perfect. All vibration was eliminated. . . . Captain Nemo never had such music as we had—Ket had it arranged so that we not only could dial from our phones any other phone on the boat, but any one of the twenty-four phonograph records— the program each day being changed and placed by each phone. Also while in the North any one of ten radio broadcasting stations when dialed would automatically tune in. . . . Of course Ket called this an experimental boat and spent a great deal of his time in the engine room and back of the radio cabinet. When the latter was working beautifully he wanted to see what it would do if hooked up a little differently. Such is the scientific mind.

In January, 1933, shortly before the Century of Progress Exposition in Chicago, the *Olive K* left Miami on the last of its major wintertime cruises. It sailed across the Gulf of Mexico to Veracruz. From there Kettering and his party went to Mexico City and visited other points of interest in that area. In Mexico City the men went to see a bullfight. But Kettering did not go with them, for he does not like to see animals treated as they are in such a spectacle.

The most memorable event of that voyage was a severe storm in the Gulf of Mexico. The boat was sailing along in nice weather when about eleven o'clock in the forenoon the storm struck. It was a norther and it came up like a sudden fog, said Captain Shaughnessy. The captain headed the boat into the fierce wind and kept the engines turning the propellers just enough to hold position in the face of the blast and the mountainous waves. The storm lasted more than twenty-four hours before its fury was spent, during much of which time the passengers lay on the floor of the library as the only place they could stay with any comfort.

But, thanks in part to the stabilizer with which the *Olive K* was equipped, they rode out the storm without any damage whatever. After the wind had died down sufficiently, they took bearings and found that during the storm the boat had moved forward only forty miles.

Soon after the construction of the little three-car streamline train, *Pioneer Zephyr,* Kettering and H. L. Hamilton agreed that the small train with 600-horsepower engine was not the right way to use diesel power in railroad passenger service. They thought the diesel ought to be used to pull trains of full size and trains made up in whole or in part of present cars, if need be. In accordance with that view, a full-power diesel locomotive was designed by Chief Engineer Dilworth.

The construction of that locomotive was completed in June, 1935. To the railroad man, such a locomotive was surely odd-looking. In each of two boxcar-type units were two 900-horsepower diesel engines, a total of 3,600 horsepower. Underneath each unit were two four-wheel trucks with an electric traction motor on each axle, the power for which was furnished by generators in the car above driven by the diesel engines. There were no big drive wheels and no side rods, nor any smoke or cinders. There was no steam whistle, either, but instead an air-vibrator horn. Later, when the steam locomotive had been largly superseded by the diesel, people sometimes spoke with nostalgia about the passing of the steam whistle, so much so that some railroads brought that whistle back.

When that strange-looking locomotive was coupled to standard passenger trains, railroad men were astonished at what it could do. Pulling from a standstill, it could exert nearly twice as much tractive effort as a good-sized steam passenger locomotive, starting trains without any jerk. After a demonstration run from Washington to Chicago, one admiring railroad man exclaimed: "She's the pullingest animal on rails!"

Not that that new diesel locomotive was free of all difficulties. Mechanical and electrical bugs of many kinds appeared. Scored liners, broken gears and pinions, burned-out traction motors, and many other troubles were common at first. But gradually such difficulties were eliminated.

Now the real revolution on the railroad was about to begin with the gradual supersedence of the steam locomotive by the diesel on passenger trains of standard weight and length. General Motors then took what Sloan called a "bold step" and decided to build a diesel locomotive plant to supply motive power for railroads. The plant was located on the outskirts of the town of La Grange, just a few miles from Chicago.

The locomotive was now redesigned and many changes based on experience gained were incorporated in the new design. An important innovation was that the engineer had a heated cab closed off from the engine compartment. There he had a comfortable seat, a windshield of safety glass with wiper, defroster, sunglare shield, and no-draft windows. It was a place where he could work with clean clothes and a white collar. The idea of building the locomotive in units which could be coupled together—two, three, or four of them as needed—and controlled from one engineer's position was retained.

A man who had a part in these developments was Gene Kettering, who had now grown up and become, like his father, an experimenter and creative engineer. After his years at Cornell University, Gene's first job was in the experimental department at the Cleveland Diesel Engine Division. And, as that activity was expanded because of its growing usefulness in the company's business, Gene came to have a principal part in it. Thus he had a hand in the development of the unit injector and in overcoming the difficulties with pistons and piston rings that had always been a serious shortcoming of the diesel engine.

Then, after moving to the Research Laboratories at Detroit for eighteen months and helping to design a modification of the new diesel engine especially adapted to the railway locomotive, Gene went with it to the Electro-Motive Division at La Grange to become before long assistant chief engineer of Electro-Motive and right-hand man to Chief Engineer Richard Dilworth. In that capacity he made such a good record that some ten years later, in 1948, on the recommendation of Dilworth, he was made chief engineer of Electro-Motive. Thus he has had a key part in the rapid revolution on the railroad, the supersedence of the century-old steam locomotive by the diesel.

Gene had meanwhile married the sweetheart of his school days, Virginia (Ginny) Weiffenbach. They have three children: Charles Franklin II (Chuck), Jane, and Susan. Chuck's birthday is August 30, the day following that of his grandfather. It became a family custom each twenty-ninth day of August to celebrate together the birthdays of the two Charles F. Ketterings.

During the period when the first full-scale diesel locomotive was being designed and constructed, several more light-weight diesel-powered streamline trains had been built and put into service: the Santa Fe *Super Chief,* the Burlington

Twin Zephyrs, the Union Pacific *City of San Francisco* and *City of Los Angeles,* the Illinois Central *Green Diamond,* the Rock Island *Rockets,* and the Boston and Maine *Flying Yankee.* These were so exciting to people that some had waiting lists. Departure times for the new trains to the West Coast came to be called "sailing dates," and people went down to the station to see their friends off.

Progress in providing diesel power for the railroads was not made without opposition, however. Shortly after the locomotive plant at La Grange had been built and diesel locomotives had begun to be delivered to the railroads, a topside man of one of the manufacturers of steam locomotives in an address before one of the engineering societies attempted to show that the diesel locomotive never could do the really hard jobs on a railroad.

His address was quoted so widely that executives at Electro-Motive, in their struggles to get a new business going, were disturbed by publicity so unfavorable to the diesel. Volney Fowler, who had been designated to handle public relations and advertising for Electro-Motive, talked the matter over with H. L. Hamilton, general manager of the division. They agreed that they ought to have something to answer the argument of that address, and that it would have to come from someone whose opinions bore considerable weight. So Fowler was commissioned to approach Kettering on the subject.

He went at once to see Kettering. "I jumped right into the subject," Fowler said, "and Mr. Kettering patiently heard me out on the proposal that he use one of his speaking invitations . . . to knock the props from under that person."

Fowler recalled: "He looked at me sort of sorrowfully and said: 'Fowler, I'm disappointed in you. And you call yourself a publicity man. Why, don't you know, young man, that the finest asset we have for our diesel locomotive business is the fact that all our competitors believe we are crazy? If you will help them keep on thinking that, we'll not be bothered with competition during the years in which Electro-Motive is working out the bugs and developing a really good locomotive.'

"I took Boss Ket's admonition to heart, partially just for the fun of it and somewhat out of curiosity to see how it would work, and it worked like a charm. By the time the opposition awoke to what was happening, the rush to diesel power was on in full force, and to stay in business they had to make hasty, ill-prepared entries into the field."

In those early years of the diesel-powered locomotive, when things were in a state of rapid evolution and improvement, a railroad executive asked Kettering, "Why don't you people bring out new things so they won't cause any trouble or have to be changed?"

"Because we don't know how to do that," Kettering said. "You cannot start to do a new thing and hit it right the first time."

"Why can't you?"

"Well, you have no doubt heard Fritz Kreisler play his violin. He has been doing that for many years. What chance do you think we would have to take up the violin and play as flawlessly as Kreisler does? I have never found a fellow yet who on the day he bought his violin ever gave a satisfactory concert in Carnegie Hall. You have very much the same thing here. We have a good fiddle, there is no question about that, but we have got to do a lot of practicing with it." At another time he said: "Whenever a fellow is learning a new language he still speaks with the accent of the old."

But by 1939 most of the faults of early passenger locomotives had been corrected, and the railroads had come to accept them as a big advance. From then on the rise in demand for diesel locomotives became so rapid that, in spite of their best efforts, the Electro-Motive people could not keep pace with it. Straining to do so, they expanded the factory again and again, until Kettering remarked that a mistake they had made at the outset was that they did not put the back end of the plant on wheels.

The problem of supplying diesel locomotives was made bigger by the circumstance that, beginning about 1940, after a lot of development and over 80,000 miles of hard experimental hauling service on twenty railroads, Electro-Motive offered the railroads a diesel-powered freight locomotive, too. And that soon took hold in a big way as the railroads discovered its eminent advantages in serviceability and economy.

Soon other locomotive makers got into the business and over 95 per cent of all locomotives manufactured were diesel-powered. The prediction Kettering had made so confidently and so early, that the diesel engine would revolutionize the powering of railroads, was rapidly being fulfilled. Already there are several railroads which no longer operate any steam locomotives at all but are completely dieselized.

Some of the reasons for the rapid changes involved in these events were given by James M. Symes, president of the Pennsylvania Railroad, speaking in Chicago in September, 1955. "The greatest single contribution to the economic and efficient operation of our railroads during my forty years of association with the industry," said Mr. Symes, "has been the development of the diesel locomotive. We all know the important part General Motors has played in that development. . . . I would guess that this development alone is saving the railroads a minimum of five hundred million dollars a year—with initial investments being paid off in three or four years."

"What is the drawbar pull of your diesel locomotives?"

Kettering was once asked. "I don't remember what it is in pounds," he replied, "but I have been told by the railroad people that it has been strong enough to pull thirty railroads out of the hands of receivers."

Kettering has been fortunate in the extent to which he has been able to participate in and enjoy the results of the developments in which he has had such a paramount part. He has often been invited to take part in initiating new runs and in celebrating anniversaries by riding on diesel-powered trains as an honored guest. He has served on such occasions as an effective salesman for the extension of diesel power on the railroads.

The railroad was only one of several areas where Kettering's diesel developments proved eminently useful. A notable other use was in the Navy. Admiral S. M. Robinson, former chief of the Bureau of Engineering of the U.S. Navy, recalled that when Kettering began to give attention to the diesel engine the Navy was importing foreign diesels. Not only were those foreign engines not suitable for the service they had to meet, but also Navy men were apprehensive about the certainty of availability in the event of war. The two-cycle diesel engine, as developed under Kettering's direction, was, said Admiral Robinson, an outstanding contribution to the success of the U.S. Navy.

The first use by the U.S. Navy of the two-cycle diesel engine which came out of that development program was in the submarine *Shark*, constructed in the 1930's. Fitted with four of those new-type diesel engines, each of 1,300 horsepower, it had in total horsepower over 5,000. That power, delivered through an electric drive, made the *Shark*, and the *Pike, Tarpon,* and *Porpoise,* constructed soon after, the first submarines able to keep up with the fleet and to maneuver with it.

As time went on, the two-cycle diesel engine was improved further still and its usefulness was greatly extended. When World War II came, such engines of various sizes were used by the Navy not only in submarines but also in submarine tenders, fleet tugs, tank lighters, destroyer escorts, sub chasers, PC boats, SC boats, LST's, and in numerous other applications by both the Navy and the Army.

The peacetime uses of the diesel engine developed under Kettering's guidance are not by any means limited to the railway locomotive. The engine is used also to power many kinds of marine craft. It is used extensively in buses and trucks on the highway. It is used in the oil fields and in pipeline pumping stations. It is used in tractors, in road machinery, in construction equipment, in industrial power plants, and in many other places.

So versatile and useful has that two-cycle diesel engine proved to be that by 1955 the three General Motors divisions organized to manufacture the various sizes and adaptations of it had built 100 million diesel horsepower. To celebrate that accomplishment and to show the many uses to which the engines have been applied, a spectacular "World's Fair of Power," called "Powerama," was held in Chicago. That show, with its sparkling lights, brilliant colors, and many interesting exhibits, was set up on the shores of Lake Michigan on the same site as the Century of Progress Exposition in 1933 in one of the buildings of which the first two diesel engines of the new type had run, and it was visited by more than two million persons. All this came out of what began in the 1920's as one of Kettering's intellectual golf games, which he defined as "something you do when you have nothing else to do."

About the time the diesel locomotive had begun to make headway on the railroad, Kettering planned to make changes

in the *Olive K*. If he was to have a yacht, he wanted one powered by the improved diesel engine that had come out of his
own developmental endeavors. He thus formed a plan either
to replace the engines in the *Olive K* with new ones or to sell
it and build another yacht.

But, partly because those were depression years, partly because the Cleveland Diesel Engine Division was finding it
difficult to meet the mounting demands for the new diesel,
and partly because Kettering's research activity and interest
had shifted somewhat meanwhile, he did not carry out his
plans. After keeping the second *Olive K* for some time, and
using her very little in later years, he sold the boat.

The purchaser of the second *Olive K* was the Sandy Hook
Pilots' Association. The new owners changed the name to
the *New Jersey,* and for many years it has operated as a pilot
boat in New York Harbor.

Writing several years later in response to a letter received
from Daniel H. Cox, of Cox and Stevens, congratulating him
on his seventieth birthday, Kettering thanked Cox again for
his part in designing the *Olive K* and said: "The *Olive K*
was a great laboratory and from it came a whole new conception of diesel engines."

XVII

THE FIELD OF MEDICINE is of special interest and concern to Kettering. Among his friends and acquaintances have been many doctors, he has often been a guest speaker at medical meetings, and on his own account he has long been doing what he could to stimulate and subsidize medical research. In 1927, as a result of medical investigations in which he had been interested before, he founded and endowed the Charles F. Kettering Foundation to do research with the aim of benefiting mankind.

One of the early projects under his foundation was research on induced fever therapy conducted over a period of more than ten years at the Miami Valley Hospital in Dayton, Ohio. That endeavor came out of a meeting at Kettering's home attended by Dr. Paul de Kruif, Dr. Walter Simpson, pathologist and investigator at the Miami Valley Hospital, and Dr. Fred K. Kislig, chief-of-staff at the same hospital. Dr. Kislig was a practicing urologist who had acquired a background of experience in the malarial treatment of syphilis of the central nervous system. But fever treatment by means of malaria was hazardous and sometimes caused the death of the patient. A method of artificially inducing fever that would be more comfortable and less dangerous to the patient was desired.

Some time before that Dr. Willis R. Whitney, director of research at the General Electric Company, had observed that the short-wave radio operators maintaining contact with Admiral Richard E. Byrd during his South Pole Expedition developed fever while on duty. Because fever had been found promising as a therapeutic agent, Dr. Whitney built a short-wave device based on that observation to generate fevers. He called it a "radiotherm."

As a result of the discussion at his home that day, Kettering asked Dr. Whitney to make a radiotherm and sell it to him for experimental use by Drs. Kislig and Simpson at Miami Valley Hospital. Dr. Whitney thought his fever machine still too highly experimental for that. But, because of his friendship and admiration for Kettering as a fellow researcher, he did make a radiotherm for him.

Quickly it was found that when inducing fever by that means the radio waves tended to concentrate in the drops of sweat on the patient's skin during the fever treatment. This sometimes produced an arc which burned the patient. To remove that hazard, Kettering suggested surrounding the patient with a cabinet and blowing a stream of warm dry air over him. And that cured the trouble of arcing and burning.

Then he arranged for Edwin C. Sittler, an experimental engineer at the Frigidaire Division of General Motors, to give a part of his time, and later all of it, to the cabinet and air-conditioning phase of the fever therapy research project. As the experiments progressed, the cabinet passed through different models, in each of which the degree of control and the perfection of air conditioning were improved.

This went on until one fortunate day when, generating fever in a patient, the operator forgot to turn on the switches of the radiotherm. But the patient developed fever anyway, and in the usual time.

This discovery led to a greatly simplified fever cabinet, one that depended for inducing fever only upon controlling the temperature, the rate, and the relative humidity of the air passing around the patient in the cabinet. With the aid of the Frigidaire Division, a large number of these improved fever machines were then constructed and furnished on loan to more than fifty hospitals in the United States and abroad, all of which collaborated in the fever therapy research project. Applications for hypertherms, as they were called, were received from over three hundred hospitals.

But it had taken many months to reach that stage of progress in apparatus and procedure. In the meantime, much work had been done in the treatment of patients, and a host of other difficulties had been overcome. One of these difficulties was that at the outset patients undergoing the long treatment in the fever cabinet often developed disturbing symptoms—nausea, vomiting, abdominal cramps, or frightening drops in blood pressure. It took some months to find out that these disturbances were caused by the loss of salt from the system through the profuse sweating that went with treatment. After that discovery, such troubles were averted by the simple means of giving the patients salty water to drink while in the fever cabinet.

In the research at Dayton—conducted mostly under the guidance of Drs. Walter M. Simpson and H. Worley Kendell —the use of artificial fever was devoted largely to the cure of venereal diseases, particularly the distressing and fatal after-effects of syphilis. In this field the need for fever therapy was so great and the effectiveness of it so often beyond belief that, as Dr. Kendell said, the harder they tried to get away from VD the deeper they got into it. But artificial fever proved to be of great value also in the treatment of several nonvenereal diseases, such as chorea (St. Vitus's dance) and other manifestations of rheumatic fever, undulant fever, infectious diseases of the eyes, and certain forms of infectious arthritis.

An example of the severe cases treated by fever therapy was that of a man suffering from an advanced stage of syphilis of the joints and nervous system. When he came into the hospital he was in pain and so completely immobile that he

Early model 2-cycle diesel engines developed under Kettering's initiative and guidance. These engines furnished light and power for the GM Building at the Century of Progress Exposition, Chicago, 1933.

The second *Olive K* cruising on the Great Lakes.

Receiving in 1937, with three other pioneers in artificial fever research, the award *Chevalier de Légion d'Honneur.* From the left: Dr. Walter M. Simpson, Kettering, Count Charles de Ferry de Fontnouvelle, French Consul General, New York, Dr. Willis R. Whitney, and Dr. William Bierman.

Kettering, Alfred P. Sloan, Jr., and Dr. C. P. Rhoads inspect plans for the Sloan-Kettering Institute for Cancer Research.

could not even feed himself. Given the fever treatment, he was quickly out of pain. Before long he could move his arms and legs. Then, with leg braces, he could get around on crutches. Soon he could walk without crutches. And afterward he became completely normal in his movements.

During the period of research on fever therapy, Kettering often visited the hospital. For a long time he was there nearly every weekend, Dr. Simpson recalled, and often he would spend all day Sunday. He not only furnished ideas for improving the apparatus and techniques, he also took an active interest in the progress of the patients.

Once when he was visiting there a man sweating out the long hours of treatment in the fever cabinet—a down-and-outer who through the distressing effects of chronic syphilis had become a derelict without hope but was now being restored to health and self-respect—asked him, "Are you Mr. Kettering?"

When he replied, "Yes, I am," the fever patient said: "I have hoped that I might see you, Mr. Kettering, because I want to thank you with all my heart for the wonderful thing being done for me here."

Another case was that of a young man with an excellent position in the city who one day early in the research on fever therapy came in to see Dr. Simpson, "You've got to give me those fever treatments," he said, "or I'm simply going to end it all by running the engine of my car in the garage with the door shut." He had neurosyphilis in an advanced stage and knew that he was doomed to suffering and an early death.

Dr. Simpson saw to it that he was given the fever treatment and soon he was cured completely. Several months later he called Dr. Simpson and asked if he might come in and give him a special report of progress. He presented him-

self with his wife, and the report he brought was a baby--
a fine baby of their own.

In 1942 Paul de Kruif published an article in *Reader's
Digest* on how to cure syphilis in one day. The article was
based chiefly on work of the men in the Kettering Institute
for Medical Research, as it had come to be called. Out of
what he had observed there, de Kruif wrote that syphilis in
its primary stages could be cured in one day by combining
fever and chemotherapy, using bismuth and arsenicals.
There was much disbelief of what de Kruif had written, and
no little criticism of it in medical circles. But thousands of
letters came from people wanting to be cured.

Soon afterward a special hospital for the treatment of
venereal diseases by fever therapy was set up in Chicago.
This was made possible by a combination of the interest of
Surgeon General Thomas Parran in combating the menace
of syphilis; of the desire of Dr. Herman N. Bundesen, president of the Chicago Board of Health, to do something effective about the critical wartime situation in Chicago; of
financial support by the Federal Works Agency, the U.S.
Public Health Service, the state of Illinois, and the city of
Chicago; all this supplemented by the large contribution
Kettering made of fever machines and trained personnel
from the activity at Dayton. Known as the Chicago Intensive
Treatment Center, it was put into commission in short order
by reconditioning the old Wesley Memorial Hospital. Dr. H.
Worley Kendell, together with an experienced staff of nurse-
technicians, went from Dayton to take charge of fever ther-
apy at the new hospital.

During the wartime years following, many hundreds were
cured of venereal diseases there. As the program progressed
and the good results of it began to be apparent, some of
those who before had been severely critical became strong
in approval.

But soon came something new that brought a sweeping change, almost a turn of the tide. This was penicillin, which was found to be active against the syphilis spirochete. At first the new-found effectiveness of penicillin was used in conjunction with artificial fever. Later still, penicillin alone was found to effect cures of syphilis in its primary stages. In the afterstages of the disease, though, when the nervous system of the patient was affected, a combination of artificial fever with penicillin was still sometimes needed to obtain complete cures.

Nevertheless, the discovery of the remarkable effectiveness of penicillin for curing venereal diseases and allied ailments cut down the field of fever therapy on which so much fine work had been done and which had seemed destined to fill a large need in the field of medicine.

But that the fever therapy train had had to take the siding on some branches to let something new pass by was not surprising to Kettering. He had seen such things happen before. It is one of his sayings that "The front of development is not a straight line; it is a very ragged line." He has said, too, that changes are just practice shots on the course of progress.

It is impossible to know, said Dr. Kendell, how many lives were affected through the fever therapy project fostered and supported by Kettering for so long, but it was a large number. Dr. Bundesen, out of his experience, said that the availability of fever therapy when the war came "turned a health officer's nightmare into a happy dream."

Another important field of medical research in which Kettering has long been active is that of cancer. He first supported cancer research independently. Through the Charles F. Kettering Foundation he financed for some years a program of cancer research directed by Dr. E. V. Cowdry at

Washington University in St. Louis. Since 1945, when Alfred
P. Sloan, Jr., established the Sloan-Kettering Institute for
Cancer Research in New York, with Dr. C. P. Rhoads as
director, Kettering has made important contributions to that
endeavor also. This has been both in respect to such guidance as he could give and to financial aid through his foundation.

Something of Kettering's views on the cancer problem at
that time he wrote as follows: "Every problem has to be
approached from the standpoint of the prospector and the
miner. Some people like to prospect, but all the prospecting
in the world will not bring ore to the smelter. So, some place
along the line, you have to begin to work the claims. . . .
It is my impression that today we have too many prospectors
in the cancer research field and not enough miners."

Referring to the common notion—but to him the quite
mistaken notion—that no researcher should ever be *asked*
to do any specific thing, he said this: "Now, what I want to
do is to ask some fellows to do some very special and perhaps
distasteful types of things. It is my impression that if we
don't do this people will be dying from cancer a thousand
years from now."

But, in saying what he did, Kettering did not want to sup-
press originality in any way. Once, another man who was
doing much to support research on cancer suggested to Kettering that—to get better coordination in cancer research
and to avoid duplication of effort—the two of them go together and try to organize all the cancer studies in the nation
and get them under one common head, or guidance.

No, said Kettering, he would not favor that at all. "I'm
afraid of a single direction in such things," he said, and
added: "It is too likely to steer the endeavor down one road,
which may turn out to be the wrong road."

"I'm not worried about the duplication of effort in research," he said at another time. "Such duplication is sometimes a good thing. It is not what two groups do alike that matters. It's what they do differently that is liable to count."

Introducing Kettering as a speaker at a medical meeting concerned with cancer, Dr. C. P. Rhoads said that Kettering's greatest contribution to medical research was perhaps this: in speaking to medical men he had talked so often and so convincingly about the importance of not putting too much trust in existing knowledge or theory to guide their investigations, but of systematically trying things, even things which did not appear promising, that he had persuaded many medical investigators to accept his view. And, said Dr. Rhoads, such trail-blazing efforts have been highly productive in the discovery of things the existence of which had not been suspected. What Kettering kept saying was: "Theorizing is not nearly as effective as trying." In 1956, at the celebration by the citizens of Dayton of Kettering's eightieth birthday, he was presented a scroll from the American Medical Association on behalf of his "lifelong enthusiasm and ingenuity in charting new courses in medical research."

After several years association with Kettering in the work of the Sloan-Kettering Institute for Cancer Research, Dr. Rhoads said this about one important aspect of Kettering's philosophy of research: "From the day of our first meeting, he has never ceased to emphasize the points upon which his own success is based and which he deems essential for the success of any organization with which he is associated. His principal point is that if one is to have a productive career in science, one must have some well-defined objective, whether this be the development of a better engine, the splitting of the atom, or the discovery of a better means for the control of cancer. Without objectives, he feels, scientific life is unsatisfactory and scientific work in general unproductive. This point of view is, of course, in sharp contrast to that so frequently enunciated in recent years by those who believe sincerely that there should be no objective in research.

"Mr. Kettering's insistence on the correctness of his position has roused considerable opposition. Much of it is based upon a fundamental misunderstanding of what he means by his statement. He is pictured by some as being opposed to fundamental research and concerned only with the pragmatic, or empiric, methods. Of course, nothing could be further from the truth."

Kettering liked also to develop new devices for use in medicine, and he did so whenever he could. One such project in which he had a part was the development of a practical oxyhemograph. This is an instrument for use during surgical operations which serves to give warning before the concentration of oxygen in the blood of the patient falls too low for safety. It does that through a photoelectric means of recording color changes in blood hemoglobin. The photoelectric eye of the apparatus is a tiny device which looks through the ear lobe of the patient.

In developing that device, the assistance of Kettering and his research associates, chiefly Dr. E. J. Martin and Wayne Chapman of the General Motors Research Staff, was given to Dr. Roy D. McClure and Dr. Frank Hartman, investigators at the Henry Ford Hospital who were directly concerned with the endeavor. By uniting their efforts, these men took a primitive device originated by K. Kramer in Germany and, by means of a greatly improved principle, developed an instrument that could be used in the stress of actual surgical operations.

Speaking in 1948 to those present at a meeting of the American Surgical Association, Dr. McClure gave this account of Kettering's part in that interesting endeavor: "Ours is a far cry from the first Kramer machine that Hartman worked with eleven years ago. . . . We showed this apparatus one sweltering hot summer day to our long-time friend, Charles F. Kettering. Off came his coat and on hands and knees he explored the inside workings of this box. He came up with the statement that the feeble impulses through the photoelectric cells could be amplified in a different way to greatly simplify the process. . . . Today you have seen the result of invaluable improvements, thanks to Kettering."

In all, out of his uncommon interest in medicine and its more effective utilization Kettering has made and is making an important contribution to human welfare. A statement by Dr. Herman N. Bundesen, with whom Kettering worked on the fever therapy project—although a bit overgenerous perhaps—was that, if he could have his wish, he would choose to die the same day as Kettering. For on that day, said Dr. Bundesen, St. Peter will fling open the gates of heaven so wide to receive Kettering that he, too, might be able to slip in sideways.

There is a personal reason why Kettering should have a particular interest in finding a way to end the menace of cancer. That dread disease has struck especially hard in his own family. It snatched Mrs. Kettering from him in 1946 and at other times his two sisters, Emma and Daisy.

In January, 1946, Mrs. Kettering went down to Florida shortly ahead of the time when her husband was to have gone. Soon sickness overtook her. She was brought back to Detroit, to the Henry Ford Hospital, where Kettering's friend, Dr. Roy D. McClure, took charge. An operation disclosed an advanced cancer of the pancreas that had not been suspected before.

After the operation Dr. McClure told Kettering that the condition had been relieved temporarily but that nothing more could be done and that he thought Mrs. Kettering could not live more than about three months.

Kettering then gave up all his activities except some of those at the Research Laboratories and did everything he could to keep Mrs. Kettering comfortable and happy. They tried to hide from her any knowledge of her true condition, and Kettering thought they were successful in doing so. He kept the nature of Mrs. Kettering's illness from others, too, even from their friends.

Dr. McClure's prediction came true, and Mrs. Kettering died on the last day of April, 1946. That was just a month before she would have been sixty-nine. "I will always be grateful to Dr. McClure," Kettering said, "that he did not tell her nor let her suffer at all."

When on the sad day of Mrs. Kettering's funeral General William S. Knudsen—who had been president of General Motors and later director of production for the War Department—came to Dayton, he walked over to her casket with Kettering and, while standing reverently there, said, "She never got the credit she deserved."

"But I always gave her credit," Kettering replied.

"I know you did," General Knudsen assured him, "but other people did not give her nearly as much as she should have had for her large part in your success."

Just before Mrs. Kettering had gone to Florida that last time—after she and Charlie had lived nearly half their married life in the Book-Cadillac Hotel—she told Ernest Bossut, who had the care of Ridgeleigh Terrace and kept it always ready for them, that she wanted Charlie to quit work so they might come back to that home to live once more. "As soon as we can," she said, "and I have been talking and talking to Charlie about it, we will come back."

But, though the fates did not let them return to Ridgeleigh Terrace to live, Kettering said to some of his friends after her death, "Mrs. Ket and I had a wonderful life together."

XVIII

How plants grow in air and sunlight is a mystery which Kettering regards as the most important single phenomenon in the world. "It is the only way we have of keeping some of the sun's energy down here so we can use it next winter when it gets cold," he has said. "We do not know how plants pick up this energy and convert the inanimate carbon dioxide and water into the vital materials so necessary for our existence."

Yet the Lord is certainly not trying to keep it secret, he said, too, for he has it around everywhere. The leaves of plants fix billions of tons of carbon every year. "They do it without a test tube, without a burette, without a chemical balance, without a log table or a slide rule or anything else."

In an early effort to pry into the secrets of the green leaf, Kettering built a greenhouse at the foot of the hill on which stands his home, Ridgeleigh Terrace. There he and his assistants grew plants in sand carefully washed free of all sustaining elements. The food was then supplied as a water solution trickled through the sand. They observed that the plant's appetite changed with conditions. It selected a certain formula as it grew, another when it bloomed, and still another while forming its fruit. Kettering recalled that, by controlling the composition of the feeding solution, he could raise cucumbers so huge that he "didn't dare tell about them" because everybody thought he was lying.

In 1930, through the then recently organized Charles F. Kettering Foundation, he set up at Antioch College a research project on photosynthesis and chlorophyll. Those are big words, he said, which sound "as though we must be a smart bunch of fellows. When we say photosynthesis, we say the effect of light, and chlorophyll is the Greek word for green leaf. But we don't know a bit more about the green leaf in Greek than we do in English—not a bit. . . . So I told the boys, 'Let's make it simple. We will just ask the question: Why is the grass green?' "

In setting up that research he did not expect to solve the mystery quickly. At the outset he said to his collaborators: "I want you all to get married and have a lot of children, because I think this is about a three-generation job. I shall not be disappointed if I have to die without knowing, because I think some generation soon will know."

At first the group of investigators at Antioch College was headed by Dr. O. L. Inman, and later by Dr. Harry V. Knorr. Out of years of effort, those men made many contributions to knowledge in the difficult field of chlorophyll and photosynthesis. But, in spite of it all, the key to nature's magic—of how plants take carbon dioxide from the air and water from the soil and, under the influence of sunlight, combine them to form the substance of the living plant—continued to elude them.

The only really good answer he had yet received to the question: Why is the grass green? joked Kettering, came from a fellow who ran a golf club in Arizona. "The thing that makes grass green out here," the man said, "is water."

Chlorophyll is a complex compound, the product of long, long evolution. And, in his thinking, Kettering came around to the view that in studying chlorophyll they were not starting back far enough. In 1938 he wrote to Dr. Inman: "I feel perfectly sure that the fundamental reaction between radiation and chemistry had to start in a very much simpler form than is now manifest in the leaf of the plant."

He said later that trying to unravel the mystery of photosynthesis by studying the leaf of the plant is just as if one who had never known anything about the automobile or seen one, and who could get only an automobile with the hood sealed down, should try to find out what makes it go merely by examining the air and fuel going into it and the gas leaving the exhaust pipe.

He began, therefore, to think in terms of what he called prebiological chemistry. By that he meant the evolution of light chemistry back when there were only radiation from the sun and some simple compounds, before there was any biology or living cells. The key question, he thought, was how energy from the sun was first fixed and stored up in new compounds. This meant that the compounds formed in sunlight had to hold more energy than those from which they were made.

"There is no reason why we cannot convert sunshine without growing plants," he said. "We looked at birds until we learned how to fly, but there aren't any feathers on airplanes."

Once when someone asked whether we may ever be able to run automobiles by radio, Kettering said we are running them that way now. We run them on energy radiated millions of miles from the sun to the earth in ages long past, and afterward buried in the earth in the form of petroleum.

"The great receiving set is the leaf of a plant," he said, "and if it wasn't for that, you wouldn't have automobiles or anything else. Yet today, in this age in which we call ourselves scientific, we know just exactly nothing about how the leaf of a plant is able to pick up the radiant energy from the sun and convert it into chemical compounds. . . . We're going to have to learn more about how to catch this energy from the sun."

In the early 1920's, when some of his associates were discussing the grave fear, prevalent then, that petroleum would soon be exhausted, he related in a little parable what was in his mind even at that time. It was during lunch at which bean soup was served. After listening to the men talk for a little while, he said: "You know, fellows, a bean is pretty smart." Having, with that saying, got the attention of everyone, he continued: "Nature provides the bean with a quantity of nourishment to keep it going until it gets a start in life. When planted in the ground, it sends up a sprout to take a look around. There it could say, "I'll just grow in this lovely sunshine and put out a lot of leaves. I have plenty of bean meat to keep me going for a while.'

"But the bean, being smart, does no such thing. Instead, it uses its store of nourishment to send roots deep into the earth. Only then it is ready to put out leaves in the sunshine.

"Now, this petroleum you have been talking about is nothing but 'bean meat' to keep us going until we can get a good start. If we are as smart as the bean, we will, while petroleum does last, dig into the secrets of nature. If we do that, we will find other sources of energy to keep us going after petroleum has been used up."

He knew that the energy coming down to us from the sun was a huge resource. It has been computed that in only a few days the earth receives in sunshine as much energy as is stored up in all our coal, petroleum, natural gas, oil shale, and tar sands. The sunshine of a few days is thus equivalent in energy to all the fuels deposited on earth in all the millions of prior years. If we could catch only two-tenths of 1 per cent of the energy of sunshine, we would double our food supply and everything else, said Kettering. "If we don't succeed in catching at least that much, it is because we are a little stupid up in the attic. . . . And I don't think we are that bad."

So that his research endeavors in photosynthesis, and in medicine, too, might continue to be carried on properly after his death, Kettering made in 1948 some constructive changes in the Charles F. Kettering Foundation. He strengthened its financial position. He enlarged the size of its board of trustees and made his son Gene chairman. A full-time director of research was employed, Dr. Edward M. Redding, later succeeded by Dr. Howard A. Tanner. Of the new arrangement, Kettering said: "I don't want to kick the bucket, but I am going to fix things so that the foundation will go on in case I should."

The foundation then contracted with a number of universities and research institutes for the study of prebiological chemistry and other phases of the problem of photosynthesis. This work demonstrated that organic compounds could be formed under conditions which may have prevailed when the earth was quite young. But yields were very small. Nature had greatly improved the situation by evolving the process called photosynthesis. So the project was guided back along that path.

But by this time the technique of radioactive "tracers" had become available. And the foundation began intensive efforts to utilize such tracers in the chemical study of biological processes.

The earlier work on prebiological chemistry had not been unrewarding. Much new knowledge had been gained. An offshoot of that work, although not carried out with foundation support, was the development of finishes for automobile bodies with improved resistance to weathering and to fading in sunlight.

Meanwhile it had become evident that the study of photosynthesis would make faster progress if the foundation had a research laboratory of its own. So one was installed in the basement of Kettering's home. A group of research men with a variety of skills and interests was brought together there, and an enthusiastic spirit of teamwork quickly developed.

The group and its activities soon outgrew that laboratory, however. In 1953 a new research laboratory was constructed in Yellow Springs, Ohio. The group from the laboratory at Kettering's home and those who had been working on the project at Antioch College, sponsored by the foundation, were now combined in that new building, and others were added to the staff. In 1956 some thirty scientists and technicians were hard at work in this new solar energy research laboratory on various aspects of the problem of photosynthesis, as well as on some alternative schemes for utilizing the energy of sunshine.

Much of Kettering's time and interest is devoted to the research there. His tall figure is always a welcome sight to those working in the laboratory. He carries on spirited discussions with them on all phases of their work, and his boundless enthusiasm is contagious. "I know we are on the right track," he will say. "This may not turn out to be exactly as we think, but this is the way to find out."

Possessed of infinite patience, Kettering does not expect that within his lifetime a full answer will be found to the question: "Why is the grass green?" But, out of all the immense amount of intelligent effort being put forth in his laboratory and elsewhere, nature's process of fixing the energy of sunlight is beginning to be understood, if only in some small respects. "We have to recognize we are just learning how to learn now," he says.

It is Kettering's hope that in the end a better means will be found for capturing the energy the sun is sending us so freely and so lavishly—a means so much more effective and efficient than nature's method today that such energy can be made available in the greatest abundance to people everywhere, whether as food or as fuel. "If we starve to death or run out of fuel," he says, "it's our own fault."

"What is magnetism?" This question has fascinated Kettering ever since his college days. "I would like to know," he would say, "what the fingers with which a magnet reaches out and pulls a piece of metal to it are made of."

To him, the importance of understanding magnetism went far beyond its usefulness in the generation and utilization of electricity. He wanted to find how it is that forces can act through what appears to be empty space—although in his view space is not empty and cannot be. Besides magnetism, there are three other forces that act across space. One is between electrostatically charged objects. The second is gravitation. And the third is radiation, such as from the sun.

It seemed to him that, if he could only get an understanding of just one of those four forces and of how it acts, he might then be able to understand all. And the study of magnetism, he thought, offered the simplest and most promising route to such an understanding.

With the aid of some young men of the General Motors Research Staff—including Lawrence F. Hope, Joseph F. Lash, and, most notably, Gifford G. Scott—Kettering did an immense amount of experimentation in an effort to find out about magnetism. The experimentation began simply enough but got more elaborate and extensive as time went on. Because of the need to get away from interfering vibrations and magnetic disturbances, some of the early work was done in tents. Just before World War II the highly refined apparatus and instrumentation, as developed in the years of study before that time, were set up in a better test station situated at the General Motors Proving Ground in the hills near Milford, Michigan. Then, when the war was over, a new and even better magnetics laboratory was constructed outside Detroit. There the experiments on magnetism were continued under still more favorable conditions, and with precision-type instrumentation not available before.

In the years following, the investigation of magnetism was pursued with vigor. Information of considerable scientific interest was obtained, which brought outside recognition to the work both in the United States and in Europe. But the solution of the mystery—What is magnetism?—seemed as far away as ever.

In the summer of 1949, therefore, Kettering got Dr. Samuel R. Williams, who had recently retired as professor of physics at Amherst College and who also had long been actively interested in the field of magnetics research, to spend some time to determine what he thought its future direction ought to be.

Kettering's own view about the state of progress on the project is seen in what he told Dr. Williams when he came. We are down in the swamp on this project now, he said. But I think if we look around with enough intelligence and persistence we'll find a way out. This is not the first time we have been in the swamp. We were in it on the research that led to "Ethyl" gasoline and at other times, and we found our way out. I think we will find a way out this time, too.

The way to break out of a confining stockade, he said at another time, is to keep jabbing at the surrounding walls by random experiments. That way a fellow will be sure to find that some parts of the encircling wall—the wall that looks so solid everywhere—are in reality nothing but papiermâché.

From Dr. Williams's analysis of the magnetics research project, he came to this conclusion: "The more I get into it the more I think Mr. Kettering has something worth while in his project on magnetism. I feel certain that they are going to be able to pull something out of it."

Kettering wanted the project to go ahead whether or not that "something" could be got in his lifetime. As put by

Gifford Scott, the man who has worked with him longest on the magnetism research project, "Boss Ket will stick at a thing until hell freezes over."

In the years since Kettering's retirement in 1947, during which he has been active in the scattered research projects described in this chapter and the one preceding, he has depended upon the airplane to get from place to place with speed and comfort. After the General Motors Research Corporation was moved from Dayton to Detroit in 1925, he flew back and forth to Dayton for a while. Then in the late 1920's he quit flying altogether, and he did not take it up again for twenty years. Up to the time he quit, though, he had been flying so much and for so long that he is understood to have had then the most hours in the air of any amateur pilot.

After the death of Mrs. Kettering in 1946 and his retirement as head of research for General Motors in 1947, he began to fly once more. In 1948 he again got an airplane of his own. It is a Grumman Mallard, an amphibian which makes it possible for him to land on the water near his farm at Loudonville, as well as on regular airfields. He named his plane "The Blue Tail Fly," and as a pioneer instrument flier, he had it equipped with the latest in instrumentation, including a telephone which he uses frequently.

In that plane he has since traveled wherever he needed to go. It has made him quite mobile and he does a great deal of flying about the country. Although he sometimes takes the controls for a little while when in the air, he does not fly the plane himself but always has it operated by professional pilots.

He took up again his active interest in improving flight. So great is his attachment to flying that—as he told his brother-in-law, Ralph D. Williams, in 1951—he would have liked nothing better than to be able to renew his airplane pilot's license for his seventy-fifth birthday, which came that year.

Recently he has intensified his activity, especially in the field of the small airplane. He has increased the number of his own airplanes to three by purchasing first a Cessna 180 and later a Piper Apache. He would like to help find ways to bring down the cost of owning and operating a plane and to reduce the need for long runways in take-off and landing. There is a great opportunity in extending the usefulness of the small airplane, he thinks. In spite of all the progress thus far in that field, the surface of what is possible has, in his view, barely been scratched.

XIX

"MY FUNDAMENTALS OF BUSINESS are simply this," Kettering has said: "I know I can't make and sell something for less than it costs me. . . . I also know that if my product isn't worth more to the customer than he pays for it, I can't stay in business. . . . That's the double-profit system. You have to have a small profit for the manufacturer and a very large profit for the user.

"The best way to find out how much your customer's profit is is to ask yourself how much more you would pay for an electric light bulb than it costs if you couldn't get another one. . . . That's the customer's profit—and it's a lot more than they get for the lamp itself. . . . It is the customer's profit that has built this country. It wasn't built from manufacturing profits."

From time to time during his long career Kettering became an investor in many enterprises of one kind or another. However, his financial resources, which are large, consist mostly of General Motors stock. It is in considerable part stock which he received originally in payment for the successful concerns he and E. A. Deeds had set up to manufacture his inventions. The market value of that stock—representing his share in the corporation for which he worked so long—has kept increasing as the years have gone by. And that increase resulted in no small part from the pioneering efforts of Kettering himself in keeping the concern in the forefront of progress.

Of his other investments, one of the most interesting and significant was his first. This was the experimental investment he made about 1916 in the Flxible Side Car Company at Loudonville, Ohio, of which Hugo Young was the founder, as was related in an earlier chapter. For a time the demand for motorcycle sidecars, the original product of that company, was good, especially during World War I. But when conditions changed the market for them evaporated and the company had to cast about for a new product.

In the earnest search Young and his men made during that period of crisis they hit at last upon the idea of manufacturing small buses which at first were called "passenger sedans" or "chair cars." By purchasing the chassis and engines from automobile makers and modifying them as needed, that business was developed to reasonable success. After a time it was extended to making ambulances and funeral coaches. Gradually the manufacture of small and intermediate-size motor coaches took leadership. And by making rugged, dependable, and long-lasting vehicles the company built up a business which required numerous expansions of facilities. Meanwhile, the name of the concern had been shortened to the Flxible Company.

When the experiment was begun, Kettering thought that a business bringing $300,000 a year into the town would be good. But by the time the concern had been operating for thirty years it was employing a thousand persons and doing a business of over $10,000,000 a year—in a town of about 2,500 population. Many of the employees had to come in from the surrounding country and from other towns in that area.

The principal reason for the success of that business, Kettering said, was the good management it had under Hugo Young and his associates. In Kettering's relationship to the business he seldom gave advice, said Young, but just said go ahead and do as you think best. If he did make a suggestion, it was usually in an offhand way. Mostly he let Young make his own decisions and his own mistakes. That was part of his experiment, of course. But Young never made an important decision, he said, without mentally "talking it over with Boss Ket," whose portrait hangs above his desk.

The success of that experiment was gratifying to Kettering. He was pleased especially about what the business did to elevate living conditions and general prosperity among the people of the town. The only thing people have to sell is their time and effort, he would say, and the product of a factory is just a packing crate in which the people working there ship out their labor and get money in return for it. This and the many other things Kettering did for his home town of Loudonville caused the people of the community to stage a huge celebration to honor him on his seventieth birthday.

Kettering's own business affairs, which came to be much too extensive for him to handle personally, were for many years taken care of by George B. Smith. Smith was a prominent citizen of Dayton who devoted his later life to supervising and managing the personal business affairs of Kettering and those of E. A. Deeds. Smith did that job so conscientiously and so well that he relieved Kettering almost altogether of business cares so far as his own interests were concerned. Thus he set Boss Ket free for the more important, and to him more interesting, projects to which he devoted his attention so intensively.

In 1926 a concern called Charles F. Kettering, Inc., was set up as a means of handling in the best fashion Kettering's expanding business affairs. "While I had a chance," he said, "I wanted to see how they would administer my estate." George B. Smith became secretary and treasurer, as well as director, of that organization. When in 1940 George B. Smith died, the management of Charles F. Kettering, Inc., and so of all Kettering's business affairs, was put under the

Trust Department of the Winters National Bank and Trust Company, of which he had become a substantial stockholder and chairman of the board of directors. George B. Smith, and later the employees in the Winters Bank, were the persons Kettering meant when he said in 1948, "The greatest invention an inventor can make is to get a good businessman to run his business for him."

The Winters Bank, which in 1924 Kettering had saved from collapse by taking over its financing and guidance, had grown rapidly in size and in service. In a letter written in 1941, Kettering summarized events in the seventeen years since he had consented to step into the situation at the Winters Bank:

> In addition to a lot of bad accounts at the outset, we had at that time a statement of about nine or ten millions. Today we are approaching the sixty million mark with all the deadwood out. We went through all the hardships of the depression, the collapse in 1931 of the then largest bank in Dayton and the later failure of the building and loan associations, as well as the unfortunate suicide of the man who was then president of the Winters Bank. Through it all, no depositor or stockholder lost a cent, and we did not save ourselves by squeezing people out of business. We have built under this bank a foundation that makes it one of the best of its size in the Middle West.

Of major assistance in weathering the storms mentioned in Kettering's letter was the confidence the people of the city had in his integrity and financial ability. In that bank crisis of 1931, when the largest bank in Dayton failed and closed its doors, Kettering showed himself on the floor of the Winters Bank the next day, talking to those he knew and others, assuring them in his frank and confident manner that everything there was all right. He also showed himself in the other banks of the city that day. It seems likely, said one of those with intimate knowledge of the banking situation in Dayton then, that the confidence which Ketter-ing's presence gave to depositors at that critical time saved some of those other Dayton banks as well.

Two years later, in the critical period just prior to March 4, 1933, Kettering again appeared on the floor of the Winters Bank on a number of occasions and let it be known that he would protect the bank with his resources. After the Bank Holiday of that year the Winters National Bank and Trust Company was the first Dayton bank to open.

In 1935 Walter Behm, who was appointed cashier of the Winters Bank when, eleven years earlier, Kettering had come to its rescue, was elected president. He has served in that capacity ever since, throughout a period during which the bank has climbed to a place of top prestige in the community. By 1956, the resources of the Winters Bank were more than $225,000,000, and over 60 per cent of the banking business of Dayton was being done there.

One year at Christmastime Kettering wrote this to Walter Behm: "I just want to take this opportunity to tell you and your associates in the bank how much I have enjoyed being associated with your organization. I think you have done a fine piece of work, and when we look back and see where we have come from, it is certainly encouraging to know what can be done by just simple, honest methods. I want to extend to you and the whole Winters Bank organization my great appreciation."

During the severe depression of the 1930's Kettering ex-pressed some of his business views in these terms: "I under-stand that there are something like forty billions of dollars out of work in American banks. I also understand that there are somewhere between five and ten millions of men out of work. To me those things are simply the opposite ends of the same stick. If we had developed industries at the rate we should, we would have been short on both capital and labor."

In humorous illustrations of his view, he said that we are like the man in great haste to get to a destination who went to the depot to catch a ten-o'clock train. When he got there at half past nine he found to his consternation that the train had already gone. Missing that train caused him to lose business, and he sued the railroad company for letting it pull out ahead of schedule. When the suit came to trial it was proved that the train had not left ahead of time at all. That was the train of the day before, twenty-three hours and thirty minutes late.

"Well, that is exactly our situation technologically," Kettering would conclude. "We are not too far ahead. We are a lap behind."

"The trouble with many businessmen," Kettering has said, "is that they are trying to find some way in which things will take care of themselves. . . . All the way along the road of life people are looking for park benches where they can sit down and rest. There is only one place where there are any park benches, and that is immediately in front of the undertaker's office. There are no places in an industrial situation where anyone can sit and rest. It is a question of change, change, change all the time. And it is always going to be that way." At another time he said this: "I think you can write this down. You can't have profit without progress."

He said, too, "Industries are like some kinds of watches. They have to be shaken hard every so often to keep them going."

We don't know enough to plan new industries, he thinks. "You can't plan industries, because you can't tell whether something is going to be an industry or not when you see it, and the chances are that it grows up right in front of you without ever being recognized as being an industry. . . . Who planned the automobile industry, if you please? . . . Nobody

thought anything of it at all. . . . It grew in spite of planning.
. . . I doubt whether anybody was ever conscious of creating
an industry at the time it was started. . . . You get into an
industry without knowing it. Economic planning," he said
once, "is like predicting the Kentucky Derby. You are very
likely to bet on the wrong horse."

Another significant item of Kettering's philosophy of business is his belief in the need for superior salesmanship, if
new ideas are to be accepted. "The thing that is really hard
to do," he would say, "is to sell the idea of progress. So many
people are against it.

"Whenever a new idea is presented, the first instinctive
reaction is against it. Some philosopher has said that the second sober thought is always essential and seldom wrong.
Well, the only thought you have is the second one. The first
is merely an instinctive animal reaction against things. . . .
Instinctive reactions have been at work for so much longer
than intelligence that they always get the first seat in our
mental reaction. . . .

"So whenever a new idea is laid on the table it is pushed
at once into the wastebasket. Do not get discouraged at that
if your idea is right, for that is only the first time it was
pushed off." Get to that wastebasket before the janitor, he
advised. Dig your idea out and lay it back on the table. Do
that again, and again, and again. And after you have persisted for three or four years people will say, "Why, it does
begin to look as though there is something to that after all."

However, he does not favor at all what is called high-
pressure salesmanship. He once joked that he had made an
important invention—a pressure gauge for high-pressure
salesmen.

He believes strongly in the democratic system of constitutional government and freedom of enterprise among the
people, as it has existed in the United States. And he wants

nothing to damage or destroy it. "Since I have retired," he said in 1947 in his imaginative way, "I have organized a couple of new companies. . . . One is the Utopian Transportation Company, Limited. This is a nonprofit organization . . . to give free transportation to those people who think this a 'lousy' country . . . who want to go places that are better than the United States." The purpose of his imaginary company was to buy such people tickets to where they want to go—not however, he joked, "where you would want them to go." This company he called the Utopian Transportation Company, Limited—limited, he said, to furnishing transportation in one direction only.

His other new company he had organized to sell stock, he said, "stock in the greatest corporation the world has ever seen." And that company he called United States Preferred.

"We have a Constitution and we believe in constitutional government," he said. "We also believe in constitutional rights, but I don't think anybody has any constitutional rights who is trying to use them to destroy the Constitution itself. I do not believe that anyone has the right to free speech who is trying, by the use of that free speech, to destroy free speech.

"I see many, many problems in front of our country. But, after we add up where we stand with the rest of the world, I think our problem of the future is to perfect what we have and not discard it in favor of some untried or theoretical systems that have to date nothing to show for their claims. . . .

"So I want everyone to buy one, or a hundred thousand shares of United States Preferred," he concluded. "Let's keep it the greatest organization that God ever let rest on the face of the earth."

XX

"IF WE DROVE AN AUTOMOBILE the way we try to run civilization I think we would face backwards looking through the back window, admiring where we came from and not caring . . . where we are going." So said Kettering at a meeting of academic and scientific honor societies. "If you want a good life you must look to the future. . . . I think it is all right to have courses in history, but history is the 'gonest' thing in the world. . . . I want to turn history around and look where we are going for a little while. . . . Let's put a department of future into the universities and colleges. . . . We can do something about the unmade history. . . . But we must look where we are going and not where we've been."

In these statements Kettering still retains out of the past all that is good, rejecting only what has proved to be counterfeit. "Present the new as a modification of the old," he says. "The great mistake made by most reformers and developers is that they have detached their new ideas from the old. Such may be likened to a powerful locomotive all fired up and ready for work. Back down the track is a magnificent train of Pullman cars. . . . The only way that engine can get hitched on to that train of cars is to back to where it is. That is the only way any new idea gets 'hitched on,' no matter how dynamic or potent it may be. It must 'back up' to where the old and the new may meet."

As an engineer, Kettering has some definite views on engineering education. "If I were writing the engineering course," he says, "I would write only three things—four years of physics, four years of chemistry, and three years of mathematics—and then you might fill in with anything else you want, including a little economics and history. . . . The 'how and why' of fundamentals should be inculcated to form the foundation for the approach to any problem. . . . With that foundation I can take a man and teach him about a gas engine if he has never seen one. But I cannot take a specialist, if he has not had a basic education, because I cannot get it over to him if I work until doomsday."

Speaking at the time he received the Award of Merit from the American Alumni Council, Kettering told the story of his associate, Thomas Midgley, Jr. In college Midgley took mechanical engineering. But, because the problems he had to solve during his career in research proved to be so largely chemical, Midgley turned chemist. Over the years, by intensive application and practice, he educated himself to be a research chemist in such thorough fashion that when he died in 1944 he was president of the American Chemical Society. Furthermore, in recognition of the outstanding work he had done in chemical research, he had meanwhile received all four of the principal medals for achievement in chemistry.

Kettering then related that to the dean of engineering at Cornell University, Midgley's school, he had once said: "Dean, I have a young friend who wants to be an electrical engineer. What course do you recommend that he take? I am asking because Tom Midgley took mechanical engineering and turned out to be a chemist. Another friend took electrical engineering and became a financier. So what course should my young friend take to be an electrical engineer?"

Answering in the same tongue-in-cheek vein, the dean came right back with the remark, "If you have a degree from Cornell, Ket, you can do anything."

"And that," said Kettering, "is what I think an engineering education, or *any* education, ought to be."

Although he wanted students of engineering to be well

grounded in mathematics, he objected to teaching them that engineering is a mathematical science. "It is an experimental science pure and simple," he said. "You can figure a first approximation from which you can work. But to figure the thing accurately, it can't be done. . . . The gears in the rear axle of an automobile, for instance, do not conform at all to what is conventionally taught about gearing. If such gears were made in accordance with theory they would weigh almost as much as the car. The same is true of the gears in an aviation engine. But they are very successful, nevertheless. Such things are not accomplished in accordance with theory at all, but by experiment or trial."

While he did not underestimate the usefulness of mathematics in engineering, he took many a poke at what he considered the overevaluation of its place. He once said to an assemblage of engineers that the most highly satisfactory use of the reverse-curve sign of integration used in calculus is for those two S-openings in the top of a violin.

At another time, he spoke of a mathematician who had worked out differential equations for the movements by which a cat lands on its feet when dropped with feet upwards. "It is perfectly marvelous," the mathematician said, "the way those equations fit into each other. How can a cat know this?"

Kettering responded that cats were turning over in the air and lighting on their feet long before differential equations were invented. If, when a cat was dropped, it had to work out differential equations as it fell, he said, it would probably land not on its feet but on its back.

On several occasions he expressed the opinion that he could teach young men to be inventors. "I can take any group of young people," he said, "and teach them to be inventors, if I can get them to throw off the hazard of being afraid to fail. . . . A study made a number of years ago said the more education a man has the less likely he is to be an inventor. Now the reason for that is quite simple," Kettering said.

"It is because throughout his life he has been taught the danger of failure. From the time he enters the first grade until he graduates from the university he is examined three or four times each year, and if he fails he is out and in many cases disgraced; while in research and inventions work you fail hundreds and even thousands of times; and, if you succeed once, you are in.

"It therefore seems that the only factor which needs to be corrected is to teach the highly educated person that it is not a disgrace to fail and that he must analyze every failure to find its cause. We paraphrase this by saying, 'You must learn how to fail intelligently.' . . . For failing is one of the greatest arts in the world. . . . Once you've failed, analyze the problem and find out why, because each failure is one more step leading up to the cathedral of success. The only time you don't want to fail is the last time you try."

Because in Kettering's view the field of human knowledge is so far from complete, he thinks our schools ought to teach that we know very little about anything. "Our educators should simply say to the student that this is the best package we can give you today." He often told this story about a friend of his who was a teacher of medicine in one of the universities. In the professor's final lecture to his class he spoke about as follows: Gentlemen, during the months we have spent together, I have given you the best information there is about the practice of medicine. The textbooks we have used are the most widely accepted and reliable. I have cited the best case histories I could find. But, before we part, I want to caution you that the science of medicine is moving forward so rapidly that in a few years perhaps half of what I have taught you will prove not to be so. And, unfortunately, I cannot tell you which half it will be.

In education for life, and especially in the field of engineering, the cooperative plan is best, Kettering believes. This is the plan by which the student alternates between going to college and working in industry or elsewhere at some activity related to his college course. With his gift for graphic speech he said that in cooperative education we lap-weld a fellow on to life instead of butt-welding him on. His interest in that form of education began almost at the beginning of it, as instituted by Professor Herman Schneider at the University of Cincinnati in 1906. Kettering did much to aid the early efforts of Professor Schneider, and ever since has continued to help foster the cooperative plan in education.

"The greatest thing that most fellows are lacking today," he has said, "is the fool trait of jumping into something and sticking at it until they come out all right." It was out of his belief in the need for young people to meet up with some really difficult tasks that must be done that he said, too: "Men who come up 'the hard way' usually try to make things as easy as possible for their children, thus denying them the discipline of struggle . . . that worked so well in their own cases. . . .

"Every time a youngster has to face a first-class difficulty and masters it, his wings become that much stronger. Every time he makes a choice and acts on it, boldly and decisively, he is girding himself anew with confidence and courage.

"There are two kinds of courage. One is a spontaneous explosion of aroused instincts to meet some sudden emergency; the other is steadfast and enduring against repeated failures and rebuffs. It's what boxers call 'the fighting heart,' the will to come bouncing back every time one is knocked down. All pioneers need that kind of courage, and our youngsters will need plenty of it when they plunge into the world of tomorrow."

In higher education Kettering has been a contributor to many colleges in many ways. He is valued both for the tangible assistance he has given and for his counsel. Although critical of present methods of education, he believes in the importance of education and is a devoted champion of it.

When in the early 1920's Antioch College—founded in 1853 by Horace Mann—was revived and reorganized under a new plan by Arthur E. Morgan, Kettering was one of the first to become interested. The plan to apply the cooperative system there appealed to him especially. It was Kettering, Dr. Morgan said, who in major part made the first three years of the new Antioch College possible, and thus its future as well. He has long served as a trustee of the college. He built for it a much-needed science building. He set up and supported there, too, some of his early research on photosynthesis. He has also given the college a building for its library and another to serve as a student union. To honor Mrs. Kettering, the college has named the library building the Olive Kettering Library.

Kettering has given active support to several other colleges also. With the encouragement of gifts from him and the Charles F. Kettering Foundation, Earlham College strengthened her faculty in the sciences and—in the words of President Thomas E. Jones—"embarked on a program of soils research which cut across departmental lines and fired the scholarly interests of teachers and advanced students. . . . By making liberal arts education relevant to the needs and problems of a region and a constituency . . . an exciting and worthwhile educational program has been attained."

Because of his interest in a self-help program at Wilmington College, Wilmington, Ohio, Kettering gave important aid to that school. "I have always felt," he wrote the college

With Dr. F. O. Clements (center) and Orville Wright (right) when in 1939 Dr. Clements retired as technical director of the General Motors Research Corporation.

Kettering showing Robert E. Wilson (right), board chairman, Standard Oil Company (Indiana), the high compression automobile engine developed under his direction. The engine had a compression ratio nearly double that in commercial use at the time, June, 1947.

The Kettering home, Ridgeleigh Terrace, in the country near Dayton. Completed
in 1914, this photograph of
it was taken in 1952.

Mrs. Kettering in 1943. Of
Mrs. Kettering her husband
once remarked that she was
the only possession of his he
had never tried to improve.

president, Samuel D. Marble, "that the knowledge of how things are actually done as a supplement to theoretical education is most important."

For The College of Wooster, at which he himself was a student that summer of 1896, he has done many things, in cluding serving for some years as a member of its board of trustees. He made important contributions to Ashland College, situated near his boyhood home. He has been generous of his time in serving as adviser to other colleges, notably the University of Cincinnati and Northwestern Technological Institute. To his alma mater, Ohio State University, his contributions have been many, including service on its board of trustees for more than a quarter of a century. Through the Charles F. Kettering Foundation he has financed fellowship and research projects at many colleges, and he tries to do everything he can to aid education.

He has made numerous addresses at colleges at Commencement and on many less formal occasions. Of his talks at Berea College, President Francis S. Hutchins has said: "After each visit we have felt refreshed by his lively interest and depth of knowledge. . . . No student who had contact with Mr. Kettering will forget the simple direct manner in which he took up any proposition . . . from the origin of life to diesel engines, to cancer, to atomic energy, to farm problems."

Outstanding among the things Kettering emphasizes in his frequent talks to young people are the importance of imagination and originality and his optimistic view of the future. "The opportunities of man are only limited by his imagination," he will say. But so few have imagination that there are "ten thousand fiddlers to one composer."

He is continually advising young people to stay out of ruts. Prejudice and precedent, he says, are the two watchdogs at the door of progress. To one group of young people he exclaimed: "Do something different! My God! Do something different!" Of the future he said: "I think anybody can write the most fantastic thing about the future of this country of ours and it will be too little in the end."

So great is Kettering's wish to know and so little do we know, he thinks, that often he spoke after the following fashion: "We have great libraries all over the country which contain the books of things we know. But I want to build libraries . . . to hold the books that we don't know anything about—the unwritten books. That would be a great library as I see it. . . . Someday it is going to be filled."

"When anybody tells you everything is known about something, you just draw a big circle around it, because nothing is known about it," he said. "If we have two words, two names for a thing, we think we understand it. . . . I rub my hands together. They get hot. I wonder why. . . . You say that is simply on account of friction. Well, what is friction? . . . About the only definition . . . is that it is what makes our hands get warm when we rub them together. That is all we know about . . . the most elementary thing in mechanics. . . .

"I once asked a famous scientist this question: 'Why can I see through a pane of glass?'

" 'That's very simple,' he said. 'Glass is transparent.'

"I'm afraid the word 'transparent' means nothing at all to me. . . . I would like to know *why* I can see through a pane of glass. . . . It is a mystery and has been a mystery ever since I was a kid looking out the kitchen window. . . . I would like to know whether light waves travel through the glass as light or whether they are received and rebroadcast in some other form from molecule to molecule."

So often he spoke about what he didn't know that Mrs. Kettering once told him that on his tombstone she was going to carve those words: "I don't know."

XXI

KETTERING'S EXCEPTIONAL ABILITY as a public speaker is one of his great gifts. But so unconventional is his platform manner that the reasons for his singular success are not easy to analyze. He makes no pretense of being an orator nor does he have any of the mannerisms or tricks of one. His talks are like an informal chat with his audience.

However, his thoughts are stimulating thoughts and he is gifted with a special genius of utterance in presenting them. He has a knack of putting things in direct and simple terms, of using imagery and apt analogy, and of injecting illustrations, anecdotes, and humor which give his talks vividness and vigor.

In the transcript of one of his addresses on the serious subject of research the parenthesis "(laughter)" occurs forty-two times. "Some technical reports are so dry and dusty," he would say, "that if you put a pile of them in a hydraulic press and apply millions of pounds pressure to it, not a drop of juice will run out."

He expresses things, even technical things, in simple and unforgettable ways. To him a thermometer is only a molecular speedometer. Talking about the difficult subject of thermodynamics, he said that "what the Second Law of Thermodynamics means to me is that you can't push on something that is going faster than you are."

"What's the difference between a scientist and an inventor?" he once asked. "Well, if you are looking at a great loom, the threads that run lengthwise represent the scientists. . . . The inventor is the fellow that carries the threads across and ties those together. . . . If you don't think the inventor has a useful part, just try sometime to sleep in a purely scientific hammock."

Speaking of his own business, he said: "Research is a high-hat word that scares a lot of people. It needn't. . . . It is nothing but a state of mind—a friendly, welcoming attitude toward change. . . . It is the problem-solving mind as contrasted with the let-well-enough-alone mind. It is the composer mind instead of the fiddler mind. It is the 'tomorrow' mind instead of the 'yesterday' mind."

Exaggeration or hyperbole is a device which he regularly employs to lift a subject out of the prosaic. "We don't know anything about anything," he will say. Talking to his fellow Rotarians—he is an honorary, not an active, member of Rotary—about how little understanding businessmen have of the amount of time it takes to get a new thing started in industry, he said: "It is my opinion today that if we left it to a group of businessmen to raise human children in the same way as they try to raise business children a child of nine months would have to be earning its living."

The thread that runs through his speeches is nearly always the same: The world is not finished and put up in a box. There will always be a frontier where there is an open mind and a willing hand. You can't walk out without stumbling over opportunities.

Except for a few technical papers, in which he has usually had the help of someone else, Kettering's talks are not prepared in advance. Once when Joe Butz was driving him to Cincinnati to give an address at the University of Cincinnati, he asked Kettering what he was going to talk about. "I don't know" was the reply. "I'll have to see the audience first." When on another occasion he was asked whether he would like the aid of a teleprompter in an important address he was to present, he said in his joking way: "No, I wouldn't be able to know what I was going to say until after I had said it anyway."

Although Kettering's speeches have rarely been written in advance, bits of them have often been prepared ahead of time, in the sense that Kettering has thought about them. Also, he is likely to have tried parts of them out beforehand on people to whom he happened to be talking—mostly without their knowing it.

Many of his talks have been taken down as he gave them. Although his audience had understood him perfectly, the record in cold type of what he had said often gave a most disappointing expression of it. Some of the sentences were not completed and many were in such bad form that much editing was needed before printing.

Peering out at his listeners with piercing eyes, he seems to sense if they have jumped ahead to the end of what he is saying. When that happens, he is likely to stop in the middle of a sentence, hesitate for an instant, and then take off on a new line of thought. But, as has been said by Dr. W. D. Coolidge, long head of research at the General Electric Company and associate of Kettering in a number of endeavors, conservative sayings which are well rounded off do not arouse enthusiasm or make people think as do the bold, if somewhat rough, sayings which Kettering issues with seeming spontaneity.

It was during the busy Delco years, beginning about 1912, that Kettering took up in real earnest the science lectures which he originated and which he enjoyed so much. What was perhaps the most extensive and historic of all such lectures he gave on the SS *Noronic* in June, 1916. The occasion was the summer meeting of the Society of Automotive Engineers held in the form of a Great Lakes cruise from Detroit. In that lecture he included all the striking demonstrations he was accustomed to making, such as freezing flowers in liquid air, freezing mercury into a hammer and driving a nail with it, and burning iron wire in liquid air. He made striking demonstrations of magnetism, and he used high-frequency electricity conducted right through his body to illuminate a light bulb held in his hand, to draw sparks from the end of a sword, and to set fire to tissue paper. He fried eggs in an iron skillet sitting on a cake of ice by heating the skillet inductively without any visible contact with the source of electricity. He related all he said to the improvement of the automobile and the wide field for it which he said there still was.

So unusual was such a lecture among presentations to the Society of Automotive Engineers and so unique in its scientific viewpoint and outlook for that early time that it was remembered for many years by those who heard it, and often spoken of afterward. One of those present, B. B. Bachman, a young man who had had the problem of educating himself in engineering and who later became president of the Society of Automotive Engineers, testified in 1949 that that lecture opened up for him what had been undisclosed vistas. That was precisely what Kettering was trying to do, of course.

Twenty years later, in 1936, at Kettering's suggestion, the General Motors Parade of Progress was set up to go around the country for all those interested to see, and more than 7,000,000 people have since seen it. An important part of the Parade of Progress show, as well as the Previews of Progress, which came later, has been a demonstration lecture on science. Not only has that lecture been typed after those Kettering gave so long before, but it has also contained some of the very same demonstrations he used. In fact, Kettering himself gave the first of those lectures when the Parade of Progress opened in 1936.

A little of what he said on that occasion was this: "We

have just gone through a great depression. . . . During the depression people got the idea that the world was finished. We are trying to prove it is not. . . . If we had new industries both men and money would go to work. . . . We have tried to bring you here the story of industry and how it has developed and how it works. . . . In the beginning I said that we didn't have anything to sell, but we do have something to sell. We are trying simply to sell you confidence in America, American industry, and American resourcefulness. And, if you are sold, we will be well satisfied with our efforts."

In connection with the Parade of Progress an event occurred which exemplifies that Kettering is not always a good person to depend upon to make some certain arrangement. Too often he will spend time talking about the endeavors uppermost in his mind at the time and pay little attention to what he has been delegated to do.

When the Parade of Progress was to be in Washington for the first time it was suggested that the then President, Franklin D. Roosevelt, be invited to attend the preview. Kettering was thought to be the proper person to extend a personal invitation to the President. He agreed to do so and an appointment was arranged for him to see Mr. Roosevelt—but briefly. Because of the press of events then, the men were told, only five minutes could be allowed for the visit with the President, and it would be best for Kettering to see him alone.

The men were cautioned to have Kettering there at the appointed time, for the President had to work on a very tight schedule. For that reason, they went to the office several minutes ahead of time. But that day the President was behind in his schedule. When at last the signal came for Kettering to go into Mr. Roosevelt's office, he was nowhere to be seen. They found him sitting on the steps outside talking to some workmen there. He was hustled in to see the President.

At the end of five minutes he did not come out and there was no signal from the President for the interview to end. When, after fifteen minutes, Kettering did come out of the office, the men asked, "Did the President accept?"

"Accept what?" said Kettering.

"Why, the invitation to attend the preview!"

"Oh, I forgot to ask him that."

After the coming of radio, Kettering was a frequent speaker. As in his other speeches, many of his radio addresses are given without a script and without prior preparation. His informality sometimes throws into a panic those in charge of the programs on which he appears. But their fears are groundless, for he is so time conscious and so skillful in closure that he never runs over his allotted time.

At the Centennial Celebration of the American Patent System in 1936, the after-dinner program, with Kettering as toastmaster, was put on the air. The program events fell so far behind schedule that at the end only a few seconds remained for the closure the toastmaster was to have given. So, with typically effective extemporization, Kettering said: "In the moments we have left I will simply say this, that human courage, with human faith, and the proper degree of humility knows no end, and the boundless future is our territory in which we may work."

When, to save it from going off the air in 1943, General Motors assumed sponsorship of the NBC Symphony Orchestra the question arose about the intermission period in the one-hour symphony concert. It was suggested by some that Kettering be asked to fill the interim each week, and he undertook it.

In those radio talks he gave mostly glimpses of science, invention, and industry, together with some of his thoughts about them. Some of those intermission broadcasts were given from New York where the orchestra performed, but others were given from the places where Kettering happened to be at the time. One he made from his home town of Loudonville, Ohio, a village of about 2,500 people. He related the host of changes that had taken place there since he was a boy—how science and engineering and American enterprise had completely transformed the lives of those living in the town and the country around. "This little community has not had to go out and get these things," he said. "They have come to it. The radio and other developments appeared here almost as soon as in New York and Chicago. . . .

"Much that science will discover is yet to come to the farms, towns, and cities of America. Much is already here. We should analyze the process which has produced such amazing progress in the last fifty years and make sure it continues. If there is anything wrong with the system, *let's fix it*, and *not* unintelligently or willfully *destroy it*."

Although Kettering enjoys speaking and although he has always done a great deal of it, nevertheless he has a humble opinion of its effectiveness as a medium of education. Commenting on the importance of talks before luncheon clubs, such as Rotary, he remarked that, listening to such profound messages every week, you would think those men should be the smartest people in town. But, actually, "there isn't a way you could pick them out on the street."

XXII

"You might as well try to hold a fistful of quicksilver," said the late Detroit newspaper editor, Malcolm Bingay, "as to tackle a biography of the owl-eyed wizard, Charles F. Kettering." Nevertheless, in this present effort to write a simple and sympathetic story of the man and his accomplishments, it is now time to gather up the loose ends by touching upon some other significant aspects of his personality. Something should be said about his humility, his frame of mind on religious matters, his courage, his uncommon vitality, his unconcern about money, and his good fortune in having received many honors from his contemporaries. Something more should be said, too, about his fundamental and direct manner of thinking, about his sympathetic consideration for animals, about his influence upon the beliefs of others, and about his steadfast optimism.

During one of Kettering's frequent visits to Loudonville he was chatting with a group of the men there when one of them remarked, "Charlie, I believe in this 'One World' idea. Why don't you try to do something about it?"

"Why not begin it yourselves right here in Loudonville?" suggested Kettering. "You have here a number of Protestant churches of different denominations and one Catholic. Why not try to get all those churches to go together and form a single big one? If you can do that, I'll agree to help by giving the money needed to build a church large enough for everybody in the town. I'll also install in it as a memorial to Mrs. Kettering a fine pipe organ. So you can begin to put this 'One World' idea into effect right here in your own community."

The response was that you could not get the members of all the various churches to accept such a union. But the incident typifies Kettering's simple and direct thinking and his belief that to solve problems it is best to start as near home as possible.

In Kettering's view, the human race is God's great experiment. "Most people think and talk," he said once, "as though the creation of mankind was the final finishing touch of Creation and that that represents the highest form of the work of the Creator. But my contention is that the only real experiment that the Lord has ever tried was when he created Man. I think he just tried us out as an experiment and is waiting to see if it is a success or a failure."

Up to the present time, he said, Man's record is pretty much against him. "Intelligence has built up selfishness and egotism. . . . We believe this whole universe is built entirely for us. . . . The greatest battle the human race has before it is whether human intelligence is going to overbalance jealousy and egotism or not."

Kettering would often comment on how little reason for egotism we have. "We think we are conquering Nature," he would say. "Yet I have noticed that whenever anyone speaks of conquering Nature, what he really means is that he has got right down on his knees and done exactly what Nature wanted done under the circumstances. . . . If you can get Nature to do anything she doesn't want to do, I would like to know about it.

"The earth and the stars were here, running, long before we got here and we have contributed very little to it outside of fighting among ourselves. We did not do anything to make the trees, we did not do anything to make bugs and bees and butterflies; but, my God, when we do something, how we hammer our chests. We invent a camera and get all excited about it, but we could not make an eye in a million years.

"The birds and bees and butterflies have been flying for hundreds of thousands of years. . . . They must have a continual tickle when they see us try to fly. . . . The bat is a very old creature. He has this navigation business down fine. If you take two wheels revolving in opposite directions, and blindfold the bat, he will fly through the wheels without ever hitting a spoke. He has been able to do that for centuries. Of course, he is a dumb animal. . . . That is one of our difficulties right there, the dumb animal idea."

Kettering has given many other illustrations of what little reason we have for egotism. "We think radio is a new thing. But it isn't. . . . A man will look at the moon and not think a thing about it, although he is getting a message many, many times more wonderful, and is getting it by the finest radio receiver, the human eye. . . . You can point your finger exactly where the thing is coming from . . . and you measure the wave length in which it comes, because that is all color is. . . . Radio is nothing compared with sight."

"Man is very vain just now about the discovery of vitamins," he said in 1944. "If vitamins hadn't been there all the time, he would never have been able to discover them. But he is never going to give the vitamins credit for letting him discover them." He said, too, that "if we had to run ourselves for five minutes on what we know about ourselves, we could not do it."

"When we talk about science triumphing over nature," he said, "we sometimes want to picture ourselves as the gala knight of old with his sword held high and with his foot on the dragon's head, representing the laws of nature. . . . I don't like that picture at all, because I . . . would sooner picture this thing as a humble worker who is thankful that he has had an opportunity to work with these things, who is thankful that he has had an opportunity . . . to do something for his fellow men. And I cannot help but think that,

Alfred P. Sloan, Jr., Kettering, and Charles E. Wilson at the celebration by the citizens of Dayton of Kettering's seventy-fifth birthday.

With son Eugene and his family on Kettering's seventy-fifth birthday. From the left: Jane, Eugene, Mrs. Eugene, Kettering, Charles, and Susan.

as that fellow is being thankful, I can hear a little echo from the Great Intelligence saying, 'Just in proportion as you recognize your ignorance, the road for greater knowledge will be opened.' "

Not much of what Kettering has said relates to religious subjects. Nevertheless, he believes in God; and always he is reverent and free from intellectual arrogance.

His answer to the Biblical question: "Am I my brother's keeper?" is yes—yes, in the obligation to do everything that can be done to help him out of difficulties. "Let's do what we ought to do, whether it looks like we ourselves will get anything out of it or not" is a saying of his. Speaking once before an audience of young men at the Dayton YMCA, he said: " 'What shall I do to be saved?' Look after the other fellow, that is the only way. That is the whole basis of the Christian religion—unselfishness, fundamental unselfishness."

In a radio address for the Laymen's Missionary Movement of North America on Men and Missions Sunday, 1947, he said: "The recent World War developed one thing very clearly. There are certain ideologies that are not only negative to our political outlook, but are also definitely antireligious. For this reason it is extremely important that we maintain outposts all over the world where the fundamentals of Christianity can be taught. . . .

"This is not the first time that religion has been called upon to face a serious problem. But perhaps we have never had a more difficult task because of the influence of a World War, supplemented by a definite antagonism to religion from such a large section of the world's population.

"The old song, *Onward, Christian Soldiers,* never has meant as much to the people of the world as it does today.''

In a letter of condolence to Miss Minnie Farren after the death of her mother, Kettering wrote: "It is very sad that we have to lose our loved ones. But it would be selfish on our part to keep them with us always, even if it were in our power to do so; for surely such lovely, good women as your mother and mine have found a much deeper happiness than we could ever provide for them here."

Kettering's brother-in-law, Charles F. Heyde, who with his wife, Daisy Kettering Heyde, lived on the Kettering farm for many years, was a man who greatly enjoyed hunting. When Kettering visited there, Heyde would invite him to go out hunting with him. On one occasion at least Kettering did go squirrel hunting with him. But, although Kettering is a crack shot—Ivan Teetor has seen him shoot hickory nuts off a tree—he somehow failed to bring down any of the squirrels in the direction of which he shot. Those squirrels looked happy up there in the trees, he told Charlie Heyde afterward.

"We humans are almost the lowest form of animal parasite," he said once. "There are lots of dumb animals that prey upon other animals, but they are limited in their choice of victims and they have no other means at their command. But we prey upon all animals, and that in spite of the fact that we have enough brains to provide for ourselves. We play no favorites when we start out to kill and steal.

"We are nest robbers. We steal the eggs from the chicken; and, to make it worse, we use our science to make her lay more eggs so that we can commit grand instead of petty larceny on her product. And after we have stolen hundreds of her eggs we cut her head off and eat her, too.

"A lady friend of mine once told me that that day she had got her husband to shoot a cat because it had eaten a bird. She was really affected by her own tender feelings for the bird. But I like cats and I couldn't help feeling sorry for the poor cat. Some time later I was dining with this lady and her husband and she ordered quail on toast. I said to her husband: 'Here is another job for your gun. You should shoot your wife for doing what the cat did!' "

Courage is one of Kettering's most pronounced characteristics, and one which has contributed largely to his success. Not only does he have courage in the face of physical danger, as was often exemplified during his years of flying. He seems also to have a complete absence of any timidity whatever.

An important aspect of his courage and confidence is the quite unusual tenacity with which he holds to, and stands up for, his ideas whenever he thinks he is right—also the persistence with which he pursues the effort to verify and establish them, even in the face of opposition and of repeated rebuffs and failures. No matter what the difficulties or discouragements, he is so full of spunk that he always comes up fighting. His philosophy in this regard he expressed by saying that the Lord has given a fellow the right to choose the kind of troubles he will have. He may have either those that go with being a pioneer or those that go with being a trailer. As for himself, he prefers the troubles of the pioneer.

Another important Kettering asset has been his good health and vitality. In his enthusiasm, he will go from early morning until late at night at a pace that would wear down younger men. With the loping gait which he got on the farm, he has always been a great walker. Once during World War II, after a long and active day in Cleveland, capped off by making an evening address to the General Motors Men's Club of Cleveland, he walked the mile from the hotel to the Detroit boat. At Detroit the next morning, too, he was one of the first off the boat, and, carrying his own bag, he walked the half mile from the dock to his hotel.

Although at that time he was almost seventy, his hair—what there was of it, for he is quite bald—was only lightly streaked with gray. His eyes were bright, and he was full of animation and enthusiasm. His face was as smooth and free of wrinkles as that of a man in his early fifties.

Kettering is abstemious in his eating habits. He learned early, he said, that whenever he felt abnormally hungry he should eat especially lightly. He is not so careful about where he eats, however. Traveling by automobile as he did for many years, he had a habit of eating at roadside hamburger stands, often to the dissatisfaction of the men who happened to be with him at the time. But, aside from his unconcern about food, this was mostly a matter of saving time. He knows how to select and appreciate good food when the occasion permits.

In spite of the multiplicity of his activities and the long hours he has kept during most of his life, Kettering has never been hurried. He does not run around in circles but always has time to talk to people and to see things in which he is interested. To be sure, there has been mighty little place in his busy life for such pastimes as golf, fishing, or cards. But he is a sociable fellow who delights in talking to people and whose talk is so entertaining that they like to listen to him.

To members of the Society of Automotive Engineers on the day after the announcement of Kettering's retirement in 1947, Leroy V. Cram said: "Don't be fooled by that report about Boss Ket retiring. It's the 'bunk.' When a man retires he quits work and spends his time doing what he wants to do. But Ket has always been doing what he wants to. He can't retire to something he's been doing all his life, can he?"

Some aid to understanding why Kettering has been able to do so much creative work is given by the evaluation placed upon him by two of the nation's really distinguished men. The late great scientist, Robert A. Millikan, said of Kettering that he is unique in that "he combines in one individual the interest in pure science with the practical ability to apply

228

knowledge in useful devices." Willis R. Whitney, long head of research for the General Electric Company, said of Kettering: "We have never had another man like him in America. He is the most willing man to do things I have ever seen. Benjamin Franklin was a little like him. Both had horse sense and love of fun. If a fellow goes to school long enough he gets frozen in his thinking. He is not free any more. But Ket has always been free."

A characteristic of the creative work Kettering has done is that the persons most benefited are not those paying the cost of his efforts, but people everywhere. Take, for instance, the improvement of gasoline and the engines using it through which two gallons now do as much work as three used to do. Had it not been for the advances of which Kettering was the principal pioneer and the most active promoter, the three gallons of gasoline people would have to buy instead of two would cost them five billion dollars a year more than they are paying. That by itself amounts to a saving of thirty dollars a year for each person in the nation.

Needless to say, Kettering did not do this by himself, nor the other things that came out of his efforts. He has had the help of many capable men—men who have made important contributions to his projects. Nevertheless, in most such endeavors he was the originator and guiding spirit.

Because the many creative things Kettering has done in his lifetime have been of benefit not to just a few persons but to almost everyone in the nation, it seems appropriate that he should have received a considerable financial reward for his devoted efforts, as fortunately he has. But giving him something of the reward he has so well earned has been no burden to any of those he has served, for there are so many.

Kettering has always been so unconcerned about money that during his early career he was often without enough of it on his person to pay for meals and other current needs.

Frequently when out with some of his men he would find after a meal at a hotel or restaurant that he did not have money enough in his pocket to pay for it, and had to borrow from those with him.

Fred Davis remembers an occasion when he went with Kettering to Grand Rapids to address a dinner meeting of bankers. When the two men were going down in the elevator the next morning to leave for home, Kettering said, as he twirled the room key around his finger, "I suppose these bankers have paid for our suite." But, no, they had not, and the bill was more than Kettering, the dinner speaker at a bankers' meeting the evening before, had in his pocket. So Davis paid his hotel bill for him. But this was all changed later, when the men in charge of Charles F. Kettering, Inc., saw to it that he was regularly provided with funds ample for his needs.

Kettering has always been generous with time outside of his principal fields of activity. Among this multitude of activities was his service as president of the Society of Automotive Engineers in 1918 and of the American Association for the Advancement of Science in 1945, and as a long-time director of the National Geographic Society.

Throughout World War II and the years of defense preparation preceding it, Kettering was immersed in several researches essential to the wartime effort. He was on call, too, as an adviser to the office of the Secretary of War and to the Commanding General of the Army Air Forces, H. H. Arnold. Another important wartime activity was serving as chairman of the National Inventors Council. This was a body appointed in 1940 by the President to receive and screen inventions and ideas bearing on national defense, ideas submitted to it by private citizens or from any source whatever. It was composed of sixteen outstanding American inventors, scientists, and industrialists.

Up to 1946 more than 200,000 inventions and ideas had been received and evaluated by the council. Over a hundred of these were put into production for use by the armed services or other war agencies. Included among them was a mine detector, the only one that was really successful.

In the years since Kettering was fifty, he has received many distinctions. These include more than thirty honorary degrees varying all the way from Doctor of Engineering to Doctor of Laws, besides two dozen medals and awards, nearly a dozen citations and certificates, together with a dozen honorary and life memberships. Particularly important among the distinctions which have come to him was his election in 1928 as a Fellow of the National Academy of Sciences; his receipt in 1944 of the John Fritz Medal of the four Founders Societies, called "the highest distinction in the engineering profession"; his designation by the American Alumni Council, 1948, as Alumnus of the Year, "one whose life and work will be honored for all time as exemplifying the college-trained man at his noblest and best"; and the presentation to him in 1955 of the Hoover Medal for "great, unselfish, non-technical services by engineers to their fellow men."

The multitude of honors which have come to him have not swelled his head at all. He once remarked to one of his associates in his modest manner that such things don't hurt you if you don't take them too seriously. That he has never done.

Among Kettering's intangible contributions to people are his uncommon optimism about the future and his constant effort to inspire that same outlook in others. As an early and persistent advocate of revitalizing change in industry, he has had large influence upon the managers of industrial concerns. Even in the depression years of the 1930's he continually preached the need for progress. Through his frequent addresses and through articles in the *Saturday Evening Post* and elsewhere, he kept saying: "We have a great many people who are talking about dividing up what we have. We don't want to study division. We want to study multiplication. . . . Give research a chance in this country and it will start the wheels." (It was during that depression period that he himself was doing the research on the diesel engine which was soon to transform the powering of railroads.)

Talking once, when past seventy, to a young physicist on his research staff, Kettering said that in his view the field for progress is still so vast that he would gladly swap his seventy years of attainment and all he had acquired during it for the opportunity before the young physicist. He told the young man, too, that, if he should consent to any such trade, he would get much the worse of the bargain.

"I can conceive of nothing more foolish than to say the world is finished," Kettering said also. "We are not at the end of our progress but at the beginning. We have but reached the shores of a great unexplored continent. We cannot turn back. . . . It is man's destiny to ponder on the riddle of existence and, as a by-product of his wonderment, to create a new life on this earth."

On the occasion of the celebration by the citizens of Dayton of Kettering's seventy-fifth birthday in 1951, Frank Potts wrote a compact appraisal: "As symbol of progress and the American way of life—as creator of ideas and builder of industries and employment—as inspirer of men to nobler thoughts and greater accomplishments—as foe of ignorance and discouragement—as friend of learning and optimistic resolve—Charles F. Kettering stands among the great men of all time."

Dr. Roy D. McClure (left), formerly of the Henry Ford Hospital; Kettering; C. P. Bentley, a Michigan financier; Paul Garrett, a vice-president of General Motors. This photo was taken in 1946.

With Gen. William S. Knudsen (right) in the village park at Loudonville, Ohio, August 29, 1946, during the community celebration of Kettering's seventieth birthday.

Solar energy research laboratory of the Charles F. Kettering Foundation. Built in 1953, it is located at Yellow Springs, Ohio. Here an intensive effort is being made to answer the question, "Why is the grass green?"

Kettering (right) with Harlow H. Curtice, president of General Motors, and Mrs. Curtice at the celebration of Kettering's eightieth birthday, Dayton, Ohio, August 29, 1956.

ACKNOWLEDGMENT AND APPRECIATION

IN PREPARING THIS WORK the author as a member of his research staff had as background more than thirty years of association with Charles F. Kettering. The story has been drawn mostly from a comprehensive history file assembled during that period. Many of those who knew Kettering generously contributed to that historical record. To each of them I am deeply grateful.

Among these, the following twenty-four persons made contributions which were particularly large or significant:

GEN. H. H. ARNOLD	O. LEE HARRISON
W. H. J. BEHM	MRS. CHARLES F. (DAISY
ERNEST BOSSUT	KETTERING) HEYDE
JOSEPH E. BUTZ	JAMES P. HUNTER
DARL F. CARIS	R. V. HUTCHINSON
WILLIAM A. CHRYST	DR. H. WORLEY KENDELL
DR. F. O. CLEMENTS	H. C. MOUGEY
GLENN CROW	ALFRED P. SLOAN, JR.
FRED W. DAVIS	HARRY F. SMITH
COL. E. A. DEEDS	CARL E. STEEB
PROF. C. W. FOULK	DR. HOWARD A. TANNER
VOLNEY B. FOWLER	IVAN TEETOR
DR. G. B. FULLER	

T. A. B.

INDEX

accident; broken ankle, 74
accounting machine; invention of, 59-60
Adams, Charlie, 111
addresses, 215-221
air cooling, 110-124
airplanes. *see* aviation
American Alumni Council, 231
  Award of Merit, 208
American Association for the Advancement of Science, 230
American Chemical Society, 208
American Medical Association, 185
American Institute of Electrical Engineers, 76
American Petroleum Institute Award, 156
American Surgical Association, 187
Anderson, Bill, 70, 83
Anthony, Susan B., 82
Antioch College, 189-190, 194, 212
Arnold, Colonel Bion J., 107, 108
Arnold, General Henry H., 107-109, 220
Ashland College, 213
automobiles; engines, high-compression, 157-158
  ignition system, 60-67
  improvements, 132-133
  lights, electric, 73
  mechanism, 138-139
  self-starter, 54, 68-77
aviation; airplane, bombing, pilotless, 106-109
  airplane with all cantilever wing built under Kettering's guidance; illustration, facing page, 85
  flight, record, 111
  improvement by Kettering, 112-113

interest in, 87-89, 197-198
learning to fly, and flying, 110-112
awards, 231

Bachman, B. B., 218
Baekeland, Leo H., 105, 106
banker; experience as, 128-133
Behm, Walter H. J., 129, 203
Bell, Alexander Graham, 9
Bell Telephone Company, 47
Bentley, C. P., with Kettering, Dr. Roy D. McClue, and Paul Garrett, in 1946; illustration, facing page 232
Berea College, 213
Bingay, Malcolm, 82, 222
birthday, seventy-fifth, celebration, 232
birthplace. *see* Loudonville, Ohio
Blaine, Bill, 80
Bohannon, Professor R. D., 43, 48
bomb, robot ("aerial torpedo"); search for, 103
Bossut, Ernest, 188
Bostater, Herbert L., 41, 45
  with Kettering and Carl Liebold, at Ohio State University; illustration, facing page 28
Boyd, Professor James E., 43
Bradford, Zerbe C., 70
Bricker, the Reverend L. O., 90
bromine: search for, 149-150
Budd, C. E., 20
Budd, Edward G., Company, 165
Budd, Ralph, 165
Bundesen, Doctor Herman N., 182, 183, 187
Bunker Hill school house; illustration, facing page 28

235

INDEX

INDEX

Lightning Source UK Ltd.
Milton Keynes UK
UKOW02f1607201216
290463UK00001BA/106/P